LEADER

THE FULL STORY

LEADER

THE FULL STORY

KEVIN ROBERTSON

ALAN SUTTON PUBLISHING LIMITED

Leader: Steam's Last Chance first published 1988
Leader and Southern Experimental Steam first published 1990

First published in this combined and revised edition 1995
Alan Sutton Publishing Limited · Phoenix Mill · Stroud · Gloucestershire

Leader: Steam's Last Chance
British Library Cataloguing in Publication Data

Robertson, Kevin
Leader: steam's last chance.
1. Bulleid, O.V.S. 2. Southern Railway
Company—History 3. Locomotives—
England—Design and construction
I. Title
625.2'61'0924 TJ140.B78

Leader and Southern Experimental Steam
British Library Cataloguing in Publication Data

Robertson, Kevin
Leader and Southern experimental steam
1. Southern England. Railway services: Southern Railway
Company. Steam locomotives designed by Bulleid, O.V.S. (Oliver Vaughan Snell),
history
I. Title
625.261092

ISBN 0–7509–1003–8

Front endpaper: 'Leader' and dynamometer car test train at Allbrook just north of Eastleigh – S.C. Townroe.
Back endpaper: 'Leader': the ultimate experiment.

Typesetting and origination by
Alan Sutton Publishing Limited.
Typeset in Palatino 10/12
Printed in Great Britain by
Butler & Tanner, Frome, Somerset.

PREFACE AND ACKNOWLEDGEMENTS

It was with much trepidation that seven years ago I completed the first stage of my studies into 'Leader'. Little could I have imagined the response upon publication. The first printing sold out in a matter of weeks and, following successive reprints, the eventual outcome was a second volume, *Leader and Southern Experimental Steam,* which appeared in 1990. Five years on the clamour for information on the subject appears unabated – hence the combination of the two books into a single volume.

It has been my privilege during that time to receive much correspondence on 'Leader' and in so doing, to have filled a number of the gaps in previous research. For it is a fact that any research, while answering certain known questions, also yields others previously unconsidered. In particular Mr R. Eagle provided the following information on sleeve valve failures:

> The following is an original theory, which as far as I know has not previously been put forward. In *Bulleid of the Southern,* page 142, H.A.V. Bulleid suggests that

36001 working hard on the Up fast line between Allbrook and Shawford complete with dynamometer car in tow, summer 1950. It will be noted that Number Two end is leading, while the amount of black smoke being emitted implies fireman Sam Talbot was hard at work.
Henry Mayer

welding stresses deformed the cylinders. This may well have been part of the problem, but I believe that there must be more to it than this – on the same page he says that when the first bogie was test run it started at only 8 p.s.i. pressure and ran smoothly and sweetly 'like a sewing machine'. If a stress distorted cylinder block had jammed the sleeves this would not have been the case. I think that there *was* some distortion of the cylinders enough to reduce the clearance almost to nothing, but some additional force was needed to finally jam the sleeves.

The pedestal type axle boxes did not work well at first and the offset boiler, bunker and tank produced an uneven trim. Both of these factors might produce its own torsional effect on the bogie; sometimes they would tend to cancel out, but at others they would be cumulative. Would this have produced enough distortion to jam the sleeve valves? The cylinder blocks were certainly light by railway standards and may have been prone to twisting. Even momentary seizure would have caused severe strain and damage to the sleeves and motion.

Later balance weights were added, the axle boxes improved and the clearances between the cylinders and sleeves was doubled from 0.018 to 0.036, which all helped; and the oscillating motion drive disconnected from the valve. This would mean with simple reciprocating motion that the sleeve valves would be more likely to 'run in' to match the distorted cylinders, and the improved running of 'Leader' at the end of its trial period bears this out.

The imbalance at the bunker end was less pronounced and the trouble there was less serious: most of the seizures and breakages occurred at the number one end where the offset boiler was and which seems to support the above theory.

I am also grateful to those who have taken the trouble to point out errors;

'Leader' at rest, Eastleigh works yard in 1950.

B.J. Miller

A boiler for one of the 'Leader' class engines arrives at Brighton yard from Eastleigh, 6 September 1948.

consequently, a number of salient amendments have now been made. Especial thanks go to D. Broughton, R.F. Eagle, R. Fisamley, A.J. Fry, E. Houlston, P. Ineson, W.M.J. Jackson, G.P. Kershaw, H. Myer, L. Rutter, L. Warnett and C.N. Youett.

I have also addressed a number of groups and societies on 'Leader' in recent years. Hopefully, the record of the engine's achievements has thus been put straight, for previously other writers had almost universally condemned the project. I can only respond with the same words I use at the end of my talk: ' "Leader" did not fail us – we failed it, for failing to perceive the steam engine could have developed further.' For, while in this age of the microchip, 'Leader' is no more than an historical anachronism, let us not lose sight of the fact that less than half a century ago it could be perceived as heralding the dawn of a steam revival. Although it would be a fool who would pretend that steam could survive into the twenty-first century, the Stephenson engine was never fully developed to its ultimate potential.

Time was never on the side of Bulleid. A lifetime's ideas had to be compressed into little more than a decade and were interrupted by a world war and political interference. Had the Southern remained an independent concern, 'Leader' would no doubt have been made to succeed or dragged its designer with it to oblivion. Writing this in the cosy seclusion of an InterCity 125, I can only speculate on the more likely outcome.

K.J.R.
Newbury, 1995

LEADER

STEAM'S LAST CHANCE

KEVIN ROBERTSON

For Les Warnett

ACKNOWLEDGEMENTS

It was with little serious consideration that I first became involved in the research of the 'Leader' concept. But as time progressed and the whole story began to unravel it became clear that not only was an enormous amount of work involved, but also a considerable requirement in time. In order to present an objective viewpoint within the book I have attempted to judge 'Leader' from a number of distinct angles; historical, political, engineering, operating and traffic and I am grateful to all those sited below who have so willingly assisted in one or more of these categories.

Foremost amongst the credits are three individuals, Les Warnett who so willingly provided a technical description, as well as placing at my disposal a wealth of other material and knowledge based upon his own experience. Stephen Townroe, the former Motive Power Superintendant at Eastleigh in the days of 'Leader', who from this position and engineering knowledge has been an invaluable guide and mentor to the project. And finally Don Broughton for so willingly making available his unique collection of photographs – I well recall a most enjoyable evening in Bournemouth . . . !

I would also like to thank the following, in alphabetical order, space I regret precludes a full acknowledgement of each individual contribution.

Hugh and Joan Abbinnett – sincere thanks as always, H.W. Attwell – whose memories have been invaluable, John Bell, Eric Best – for a most colourful description, sorry it could not be exactly included!, W. Bishop, C.P. Boocock, D.L. Bradley, E. Bramble, P. Bramble, E. Branch, H.A.P. Browne, H.A.V. Bulleid (with grateful thanks for permission to quote from his own book), D. Callender, H.C. Casserley, Derek Clayton (as always), Barry and Joe Curl – for much encouragement, Brian Davis, W. Durban, Les Elsey, John Fairman (one of life's true gentlemen), John Fry – a sincere thank you for everything, Ted Forder, Harry Frith, Geoff Gardiner, Jack Gardner, W. Gilburt, David Fereday Glenn, Roger Hardingham, Graham Hawkins, C.C.B. Herbert, Dave Heulin, Bill Jackson, Phil Kelley, Graham Long, The Institute of Mechanical Engineers and especially S.G. Morrison, Ron Manley and Max Millard – for encouragement and valued help, Tony Molyneaux, B. Musgrave, The National Newspaper Library, The National Railway Museum and especially Phil Atkins and John Edgington without whose help none of this would have been possible, G.L. Nicholson – a most valuable contribution, The Patents Office, Reg Randell – and I thought I was a hoarder!, R.C. Riley – for much patience and a genuine guiding influence – thank you, John Rooney, Reg Roude, The Science Museum, Ian Shawyer (a valued friend), R.C. Simmonds, Roger Simmonds, Alf Smith, Mrs Talbot (for the loan of her precious photographs), Dennis Tillman, *The Times* Photographic Library, J.T. Howard Turner, Fred Waller, George Wheeler, D.W. Winkworth – for much patience, Les Wright and Doug Yarney.

Also in this section a special thanks to Lyn, Jennie, Carole and Sharon, they have had to put up with an awful lot!

Finally I would also like to thank Peter, Lyn and Joyce from Alan Sutton. Their encouragement and guidance is ever visible in the text.

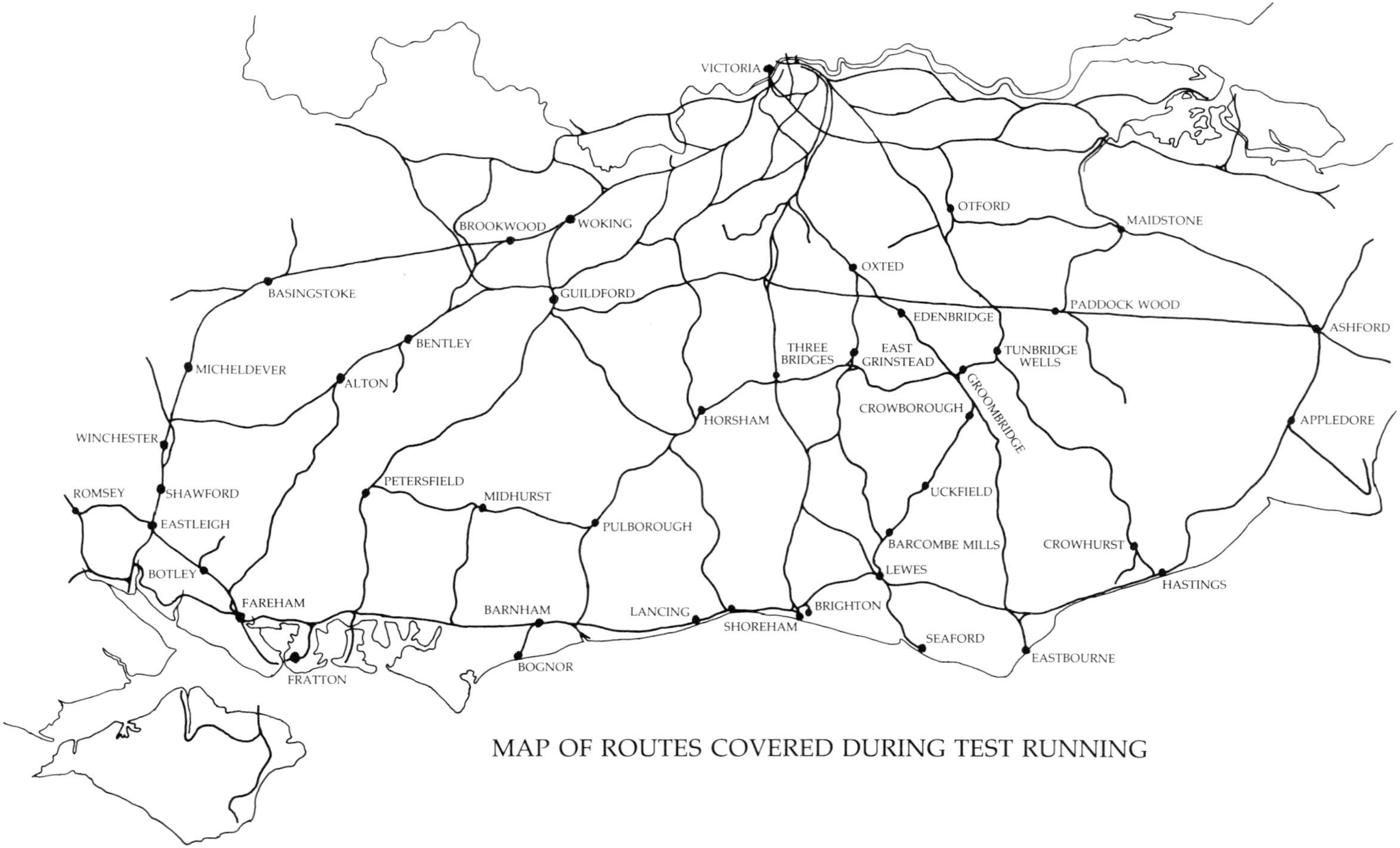

MAP OF ROUTES COVERED DURING TEST RUNNING

CONTENTS

'Leader', arguably the ultimate in steam locomotive design, certainly the most controversial. Was this the way forward? Apart from the exhaust, one could be forgiven for thinking this was no steam engine at all, showing little resemblance to anything previously seen.

Times Newspapers Ltd

FOREWORD

The author has a lifelong interest in railways and is married to a railwayman's daughter. Originally, to keep active during a period of illness, he started to gather evidence for a book on a type of experimental steam locomotive about which little had, or has since, been published.

To unravel events that happened over 35 years ago has required the perseverence of a detective and the interviewing of such elderly witnesses as could be found with first-hand knowledge. The result is a record as reliable as possible. Some documentary evidence has survived, thanks to the existence of a National Railway Museum.

Kevin Robertson has succeeded in establishing a narrative of the building and testing of the 'Leader' class locomotive beyond reasonable doubt, but the reasoning behind much of the design details, so many of them faulty, must ever remain inexplicable. You might call the book not a Whodunit but a Whydunit!

Stephen Townroe

PREFACE

Twenty years ago, the prolific railway writer, O.S. Nock, when commenting on 'Leader' said, 'I feel it is still too early to give a reasonable appraisal of an experiment which can only be described as fully in keeping with the personality and career of the designer'.

Two decades later I feel that the time may now be right, although it has become very obvious to me that there are many who still hold strong feelings either for or against the whole 'Leader' concept.

Accordingly, it has at times, been very difficult to adopt an un-biased attitude towards the engine. Previous publications have tended to deal only in the outline facts with little space devoted to the eccentricities and charisma of the machine itself. This is certainly not the fault of the writers concerned, as faced with a limited amount of space it is difficult to devote sufficient coverage to what was indeed only a part of Bulleid's life.

In attempting to present the full story of 'Leader' I have tried to present the evidence both for and against the project with, wherever possible, important corroboration. If the information has not been to hand then I have drawn my own conclusions. I have indicated these when mentioned as such in the text and I make no excuses if any of my conclusions are in any way controversial, based as they are upon the results of research.

With the bulk of official records tending to condemn the project there is a temptation to immediately dismiss 'Leader'. However to do so is to adopt a narrow minded attitude as the concept must be viewed as a whole.

I submit then my own personal efforts at recording the events appertaining to Leader, both factual and political, between the period 1945 to 1951. The anticipation, fervour and eventual defeat of this unique machine. A final challenge by steam against the diesel.

Kevin Robertson

21 JUNE 1949

To the holidaymakers of Brighton who awoke to a bright summer morning there was the promise of a fine day ahead. A day which would perhaps be spent building sandcastles or walking along the promenade and pier before returning to lunch at one of the numerous sea-front hotels and guesthouses. Any idea of work to be cast to the back of the mind, a melancholy thought banished during this the annual family holiday.

No. 36001, the first and only 'Leader' to be completed, shown alongside the main line at Brighton, 21 June 1949.

H.M. Madgwick

Who then amongst the visitors to the town on that June day realised that a matter of a mile or so from the sea-front history was being made? For on that same morning a remarkable steam engine was slowly pulled out of the locomotive workshops alongside the station to stand by the main line for all to see. 'What is that . . . ?,' one passenger was heard to murmur as his electric train slowed for the final approach to Brighton station. 'Is it one of those new diesel or electric engines . . .?' No, this was 'Leader', a steam design so revolutionary that it bore little resemblance to anything ever seen on the rails of Britain. A steam design that had been five years in development but was destined to survive less than one third of this time once out on the rails.

Despite such a short lifespan the 'Leader' story remains one of the most talked about aspects of the early years of the nationalised railway network. This is due in no small way to the project being within the living memory of many who were intimately involved, and who perhaps retain particularly strong feelings one way or the other.

Accordingly a certain folklore has arisen over 'Leader' and this is not helped by the lack of available official information under the '30 year rule'.

Why then was 'Leader' so different, why indeed was it built in the first place, and why so much controversy? These along with a number of other questions are what the following pages attempt to explain. How one man's search for the ultimate design resulted in the ultimate failure. But was it really a failure, or was it failed? That has been the outstanding question for over thirty years, now perhaps at last the reader may be able to decide.

AN ENGINEER'S DREAM

In 1907 there emerged from the Derby locomotive works of the Midland Railway a privately sponsored 2-6-2 tender engine of a unique design. This was the Paget engine and it predated a number of the principles later included in 'Leader'. (The Paget design is briefly described in Appendix A.)

After a number of trial runs Paget's engine disappeared from sight and was eventually broken up. For many years afterwards little, if any, information was available on the design, until less than four years before 'Leader' first took to the rails the *Railway Gazette* produced a booklet on the engine which contained the following statement;

> 'The inevitable question that confronts one after reading Mr. Clayton's most valuable article, is "Could this engine, with certain modifications, have been made to justify the high hopes placed in her by her designer?" The evidence, scanty though it is, seems to point to an affirmative answer.'

Could the same principles apply to 'Leader'? Time would tell.

Oliver Vaughan Snell Bulleid was born in Invarcargill, New Zealand on 19 September 1882, the first child of William and Marianne Bulleid, emigres from Britain who had arrived in the colony four years previously.

During his lifetime 'O.V.B.' as he became known, was to develop a deserved reputation as an outstanding mechanical engineer. First with the Great Northern Railway and then from 1923–37 as assistant to Nigel (later Sir Nigel) Gresley, Chief Mechanical Engineer of the LNER. However, despite his undoubted talent, Bulleid was at that time little known outside railway and engineering circles. Indeed it seemed as if Gresley kept his assistant well under restraint, for whilst Bulleid's involvement with rolling stock design is well known, there is no record that any of Gresley's locomotives owed much to the Bulleid influence.

That is not to say that these early years were wasted, for Bulleid amassed a wealth of knowledge in both practical as well as workshop practice. Indeed certain of these experiences were to come to the fore after taking over as C.M.E. of the Southern, in particular the use of welding.

Other ideas may well also have had their origins around this time. Was, the decision to offset the boiler on 'Leader', for example, taken from the corridor design of tender used on some of the LNER Pacifics? – certainly they never appeared to suffer from difficulties caused by such unbalanced weight distribution. (In the corridor tenders the inclusion of a narrow passage along one side allowed for the exchange of locomotive crews en route. As a result of this the 6000 gallons of water carried was not equally distributed on either side of the centre line. Weights were carried on the corridor side to effect an acceptable balance.)

It was not until 1937, at the relatively late age of 55, that Bulleid took over as C.M.E. of the Southern Railway and, understandably, wished to display his ideas in practice at the earliest opportunity. This first manifested itself in the design of a buffet car for the 13

'4-BUF' electric sets brought out in 1938 for the newly electrified lines in Sussex. Externally the sets were similar to the earlier '4-COR' units, often referred to as 'Nelsons', but inside the new vehicles were arranged with separate bar and saloon sections, with the tables having concave curves in a contemporary styling. A few years later his designs for carriage stock included the double deck trains, modern locomotive hauled coaches and a range of new suburban units.

'O.V.B.' Collection of B. Curl

However it is for his locomotives that Bulleid is perhaps best remembered. His Pacifics, in their original form, capable of outstanding performance, yet not adverse to lapses of seemingly eccentric behaviour. Perhaps a fitting description of their designer as well.

Bulleid's last steam design for the Southern was officially known as the 'Leader' class and was in effect the culmination of a lifetime of ideas. It was a valiant attempt to depart from the conventional layout of a steam engine and so produce a machine which would have many of the advantages of the diesel and electric engines but still use home produced fuel. This does not mean that he saw no use for the more modern types of motive power, for he was actively involved in the building of main line diesel locomotives for the SR during which time 'Leader' was at the design stage. It is more likely that he developed a wish, some say perhaps unkindly an obsession, to prove the steam engine could match anything more modern and so score with regard to cheaper construction and running costs when compared with the diesels and electrics. All this was of course at a time when coal was still the principle fuel of the nation and oil had to be imported.

This then was the embryo from which 'Leader' grew, and which was to develop into a race against time as the threat of nationalisation advanced. It is still not clear, more than 40 years later how much this race affected the final design. Or how different the finished engine was from that perhaps originally envisaged. Also how much was based on the Paget machine of 40 years earlier? What is almost certain is that the final engine could best be described as a mutant.

Typical of Bulleid was this early 1940s experiment which was intended to disperse exhaust steam more rapidly than a conventional single chimney. The purpose was to reduce the likelihood of an enemy aircraft being able to locate a train by its exhaust. 'King Arthur' class engine No. 783 was fitted with the two chimneys shown, after which a third central chimney was fitted. Besides having only limited success, the results did nothing to enhance the engines' appearance. The most marked effect when working was to dislodge soot from a number of bridges and tunnels as the blast was now hitting them from a different angle. No. 783 reverted to conventional form shortly afterwards.

Collection of A. Molyneaux

THE EMBRYO DESIGN

It was not until 1944, seven years after Bulleid took over on the Southern that the first inklings of a radically new engine began to emerge from the C.M.E.'s department. Bulleid's first thoughts centered on a self-contained locomotive carried on two power bogies.

One could be tempted to ask, why if Bulleid felt so strongly towards the successful development of the steam engine, had it taken until then for the first steps to be taken? Possibly the answer is simply that he needed to establish a reputation for himself, which the appearance of the 'Merchant Navy' and 'Q1' classes certainly achieved. The demands placed upon the railway workshops were now lessening as a successful outcome to war became more clear. In addition Bulleid was a very shrewd individual especially with regard to timing, and no doubt felt that by that date a radically new design would be more likely to find favour compared with when he had first taken office. Another factor in his favour was his personal charisma, certain members of the Southern Board and other senior non-technical officers finding him 'rather clever'.

Accordingly, these first thoughts were translated into drawings by the technical staff from about September 1944 onwards and most rejected purely on the basis of excessive novelty.

Official records refer to the project as first mentioned at the SR board meeting of December 1944, at which Bulleid no doubt wished to place a well formulated idea before

Bulleid's first steam designs for the Southern were the 'Merchant Navy' class, No. 35005 *Canadian Pacific* shown running in early BR days. Apart from some modifications to the front end design to assist in lifting the exhaust clear of the casing, the engine is basically as built.
Collection of A.J. Fry

the directors for their approval. But at this early stage it was not at all clear what Bulleid was trying to achieve, this would not be obvious until some time later.

Therefore the first drawings produced cover a number of machines which were loosely based upon the existing 'Q1' design, and including an 0-6-2T and 0-6-4T. Privately some within the C.M.E.'s department approved of these proposals, as they suggested a powerful machine of conventional design. But closer examination reveals several features that raised questions. One of which was the high axle loading of 19.5 tons which would effectively prohibit the engines from the majority of branch lines, so what was the intended use? This remains an unanswered question. Then there was the question of water consumption, for the high tractive effort of 30,000lbs allied to a 2,000 gallons water capacity would produce a working range of perhaps only 40 miles. (Conclusions on the various early designs were formed on the basis of correspondence and discussion with S.C. Townroe.)

Another disadvantage with the 0-6-4T was its rearward visibility, especially for sighting signals. In addition Bulleid could also foresee other problems, notably the long rigid wheelbase devoid of any guiding wheels, whilst the amount of weight needing to be supported at the rear was a waste of adhesive effort. These factors go some way to suggest why the 0-6-4T has rarely found favour amongst designers.

It therefore appears to indicate that other preoccupations, notably the final details for the new 'Light Pacifics' design, kept the C.M.E. fully occupied, until in late 1944 Bulleid attended one of the regular senior officers meetings at which both the Traffic Manager, R.M.T. Richards and the General Manager, Sir Eustace Missenden were present. Among the items on the agenda was an attempt to decide upon the 1946 locomotive building programme, a particularly difficult task as talk of nationalisation was in the

C16 of the Q1 class shunting at Millbrook during Southern Railway days. Forty engines of the class were built to this Bulleid design from 1942; the lack of running plate and splashers was an obvious departure from the normally accepted practice. Before the first of the engines appeared Bulleid had a wooden model in his office and apparently delighted in the surprise some expressed in seeing the new design. Others though were not so kind and asked, '. . . where does the key go to wind it up . . .?'. The departure from tradition was allegedly dictated by the need to use the minimum of materials. The same care in design was utilized in the Ministry of Supply 2-8-0's, 2-10-0's and 0-6-0T's, but they avoided the sheer ugliness. Appearances aside, the Q1 was a powerful and functional machine, free steaming and generally popular with the crews, although their lack of adequate brake power when working a heavy loose coupled train caused many an anxious moment.

Collection of M. Sumner

offing. During the meeting Richards raised the question of a replacement for the 'M7' tanks, some of which dated back to 1897. His description of the engines is worthy of repeating here: referring to the 'M7's' as ' . . . .completely out of date and inefficient by modern standards, . . . their continued existence prevents any improvement of the services they operate.'

Clearly, what Richard's was after was a large modern tank engine, possibly even the aforementioned 0-6-4T. But instead Bulleid somehow managed to get the Traffic Manager to agree to the building of 25 more 'Q1' tender engines, promising they would be better suited than the existing 'M7's'.

Naturally this was far from satisfactory to Richards and so, possibly prompted by the motive power department who were responsible for maintaining engines in traffic as well as selecting suitable engines for various duties, he wrote to Bulleid on 15 December 1944;

> 'With regard to your suggestion that the material already available for the construction of Q1 engines should still be used for this type instead of for passenger tanks, an opportunity has been taken of inspecting locomotive No.

The engine type 'Leader' was intended to replace, an M7 tank, seen at Waterloo awaiting what may well be a Clapham Junction working. No. 319 was built in August 1900, one of a batch of five engines constructed to order No. B10. The class originally consisted of 105 engines, the majority built at Nine Elms and rated at a nominal tractive effort of 19,755lbs. The design was simple with few frills, something that certainly could not be said for their intended replacement, 'Leader'. In the event No. 30319, as she became under BR, outlasted 'Leader' by some years and was finally withdrawn in January 1960.

Lens of Sutton

C1 and the conclusion has been arrived at that the lookout facilities provided on this engine are not suitable for regular tender first running. The rear lookout on the driver's side does not give a sufficiently wide range of vision, and the absence of a lookout on the fireman's side is a serious drawback, having regard to the fact that it is necessary for the fireman to assist in looking out for signals when not otherwise necessarily engaged and this is particularly important having regard to the fact that the normal position for signal is on the left-hand side. Unless therefore, the observation conditions, tender first, can be materially improved, I am afraid they will not be suitable to traffic requirements. Another point I would like to raise is as to whether you are satisfied that these engines are suitable for maintaining the necessary speeds running tender first when light in coal and water.'

The last sentence is a reference to a lightly loaded tender 'hunting' from side to side, a valid point, and one which Richard's would be aware of no doubt. Bulleid on the other hand had been involved mainly in workshop practice throughout his professional life. He had no outdoor experience, either as a District Traffic or Motive Power Officer.

With hindsight it is easy to see that Bulleid was playing for time, he had yet to formulate definite plans for the new design and so by obtaining sanction for 25 new 'Q1' engines he had at least got permission to build something for the future.

Meanwhile the test section of the C.M.E.'s department were instructed to conduct some fast test runs using the 'Q1' class. These were made over the former South Eastern main line between Ashford and Maidstone and involved 'Q1' No. C36 attached to a Pacific tender. It was hoped this would improve the rearward visibility of the engines but as the results of these trials have not been found the results cannot be known. A further step was to instruct the drawing office to design a means of duplicating the controls against the tender for rearward running but this did not prove possible by pure mechanical means.

Following a series of private meetings Bulleid and Richards next made a joint approach to Missenden early in 1945 at which the following proposition was made with regard to the 1946 engine requirements:–

25 passenger tank engines.
10 shunters.
25 'West Country' passenger tender engines.

(It subsequently transpired that 14 small 0-6-0T's were purchased for use as shunters from the U.S. Army Transportation Corps for £2,500 each whilst 32 West Country engines were built in the same year.)

However, early in 1945 Britain was still at war and as a result constraints were placed upon available supplies of steel. So even though locomotive building was taken as a necessity each new order was examined by the Ministry of Supply. Even so it was still necessary for the Southern directors to approve of the scheme and to assist them in reaching a decision advice was available from the General Manager.

Missenden then wrote a note to both Bulleid and Richards:

> '. . . . I think we might, pending a decision being reached on the question of the passenger tank engines, indicate at the next M & E Committee that our building programme will be 25 mixed traffic, 25 freight and 10 shunting engines.'

The General Manager was in effect sitting on the fence, no doubt aware of the increasing tension between his C.M.E. and traffic manager, by this then he sought to appease the situation. He was also acutely aware of the performance of the original 'Pacifics' and so perhaps apprehensive about another new and untried design. Accordingly the term 'mixed traffic' was nicely non-commital. (See Appendix B)

In the meantime the drawing office were still busy with various proposed designs, and in March 1945 produced a 'Q1' type of 0-6-0 but with Pacific type cowlings to both the front of the engine and rear of the tender. This was intended to be suitable for either direction running – presumably the difficulties with duplicating controls had been overcome although this is not mentioned.

Shortly afterwards came a variety of large tank engines, including a 2-6-2T, 2-6-4T and finally a 4-6-4T. But the latter design would have suffered from the same disadvantage as the earlier 0-6-4T with regard to wasted weight for adhesion while the high centre of gravity would be likely to preclude fast running. (The Southern were still acutely aware of the consequences of the Sevenoaks' accident in 1927 in which a tank engine at the head of an express was derailed with serious loss of life. From that time on large tank engines were hardly in favour and the Maunsell 'W' class 2-6-4T design of 1931 were prohibited from working passenger trains.)

Bulleid was also quick enough to realise the strength of opposition to these proposals and so now took the design to its logical conclusion by combining the advantages of both tank and tender engines, namely a steam engine on two power bogies. The result was a

In June 1946 there emerged from Brighton the first of the 'Light Pacifics', the class eventually extending to some 110 engines. Externally they were similar to the larger Merchant Navy's, although by the time this view was taken in 1948 certain changes had been made to the design of the cab. Years afterwards, when the Southern Region had a fleet of 140 Bulleid Pacific's, all the earlier Southern built 4-6-0's were also still in service, a surprising fact when in the normal course of events an influx of new engines would be expected to consign an equivalent number to scrap. The reason was the unreliability of the new design. At times splendid to ride on with plenty of steam to spare, master of any job and yet at others totally the reverse. In addition they were very expensive in coal, water, oil and maintainance. One senior official quoting, '. . . oil, oil all over the system'. Depot maintainance staff disliked the engines for their inaccessible moving parts and consequent unreliability in service. This culminated in the decision to rebuild the engines on more conventional lines from 1956 onwards.

Lens of Sutton

C-C type although still with many unanswered engineering problems. Of these the foremost was how would there be room for the steam and exhaust pipes to clear no less than 18 cylinders? Similarly it was unlikely the boiler could produce the steam required and consequently the 3000 gallons of water to be carried would be sufficient for perhaps only 50 miles.

Apart from this first radical new design Bulleid was also faced with opposition from within his own department. His able Chief Draughtsman, C.S. Cocks, who had come with Bulleid from the LNER, far from shared the ideas of his chief. Consequently Cocks attempted to dissuade any further progress towards such a new and untried machine.

Possibly Bulleid could perhaps already sense victory and so approached Richards with a view to finding out his exact requirements for a new engine. The result was a well known memo dated 3.8.45, although probably produced by some hard pressed clerk;

ROUTES AND WEIGHTS OF TRAINS TO BE HAULED

Plymouth to Tavistock or Okehampton	256 tons
Okehampton, Halwill Junction and Bude	256 tons
Barnstaple and Ilfracombe	325 tons

Exeter and Exmouth	384 tons
Bournemouth and Swanage	320 tons
Brookwood, or similar outlying stabling grounds to Waterloo	450 tons

SPEED OF TRAINS 50–60 MILES PER HOUR

DISTANCES TO BE RUN BETWEEN TAKING WATER AND COAL
60 miles for water and 120 miles for coal.

This was hardly an accurate forecast of traffic requirements on the first five lines mentioned. Apart from a few summer Saturdays these routes were the province of light trains on unexacting schedules.

It is therefore the last catagory that is the most interesting. The little 'M7' tanks were having to struggle in and out of Waterloo with empty rakes of perhaps 10, 12 or even 14 coaches and were totally unsuited to the task.

One is left to ponder on Richards' exact thoughts at the time. Irritated no doubt, he may well have thought '. . . all I want is a replacement for those clapped out M7's which slip and slide whenever it is wet and consequently delay everything else. I have been telling him this for months, why can't he just get on with it . . . ?'

It is worth mentioning at this point that apart from the M7's, a host of other engines displaced from more exacting duties were also working many of the duties described above. The 'withered arm', the common title given to the Southern lines west of Exeter, was the home of a motley collection of antiquated designs, most dating back to the 19th century but still perfectly capable of working the poorly patronised services. Yet only a

One of the 14 shunters purchased from the U.S. Transportation Corps for use as dock shunters by the Southern Railway. No. 1974 is depicted outside Eastleigh works in April 1947. Arguably this design could have served as a replacement for the M7's out of Waterloo far better than 'Leader'.
Collection of A. Molyneaux

few years later the appearance of so many 'Light Pacifics' meant these were to be seen on two and three coach trains over the same routes. It was not until the introduction of the BR Standard class '2', '3', and '4' tanks from 1952 onwards that a really efficient machine was available to the traffic department. Exactly the sort of engine everyone hoped Bulleid would produce.

Thus in terms of power requirements Bulleid now had clear criteria for the new design and so began to emerge a steady stream of ideas he considered worthy of inclusion. Other ideas were suggested involving a reduction in the number of classes of steam engine required. It was envisaged that all traffic would be able to be handled by the 'Merchant Navy', 'West Country' and 'Q1' classes together with two types of tank. A little later this was taken one stage further when two versions of 'Leader' were referred to, the design for the prototype No. 36001 as the smaller of the two! But this was pure ideology, for with something in the order of 2000 steam locomotives then running on the Southern the economics of such a suggestion were totally impractical.

However, to return again to 1945, for despite the problems raised by a twin bogie steam engine having multiple cylinders, the possible attractions were enough for Bulleid to set one of his drawing office staff, W.H. 'Joe' Hutchinson on an investigation of the 'sleeve valve' principle which would be ideal on space grounds for a multi-cylinder locomotive.

The sleeve valve also offered other advantages in relation to the supposed thermal efficiency, although against this was an increase in the number of moving parts and known difficulty in lubricating the working surfaces in contact.

Possibly this attraction stemmed from the fact that the earlier Paget design had used similar valves, whilst the sleeve valve was then in regular use on both stationary engines and within the Hawker *Typhoon* aircraft.

Cocks, however, again attempted to bring Bulleid back to more conventional thinking and so the appearance in November 1945 of a further 4-6-4T may well have been associated with him. But again there are variations to the norm, for example a 350 p.s.i. boiler and only two cylinders, although there was no indication as to the type of valves to be used. Shortly after this, in December 1945, Bulleid's influence once again becomes clear with another 4-6-4T, but this time with an offset boiler allowing access to a cab at each end. Oil fuel too was envisaged.

Thus 1946 started with no new design either approved or likely to be so in the immediate future. Left to Cocks the final design may well have been similar to one of the earlier proposals. A conventional tank engine utilising the 'Q1' boiler and capable of a high power output. Bulleid though once again ventured into the unknown, the next design to appear was described by his son H.A.V. Bulleid, as 'The boiler on a well wagon'. Again there were numerous unanswered engineering features.

The concept of this design was now apparent for by February 1946 a second 0-4-4-0 had been suggested, this time with a water tube boiler. Was this latter feature perhaps a throwback to the experimental 'Hush-Hush' engine on the LNER? Certainly Bulleid would have been acquainted with the design.

But these proposals were just that – proposals, without recourse to important details such as axle loadings. The 0-4-4-0 having an unacceptable axle weight of 20 tons compared with the 18 tons of the M7 it was intended to replace.

By now however, Bulleid felt he was winning and so pressed ahead regardless of the reservations of others. At the same time this haste meant he would occasionally 'forget' to liaise with the motive power department regarding the practicalities of his design. Such a lack of consultation, together with, at times, an unpredictable and off-hand manner understandably made him unpopular. He would for example override a subordinates authority in front of junior staff both in the drawing office and on the workshop floor. Apart from the resultant bad feeling, this also caused rifts between men and departments, some of which failed to heal until he left the railway altogether. There was, however, another side to Bulleid which should not be forgotten and it was one by which he is recalled by the numerous artisans at the various running sheds. This shows him to be a genuine, caring man, who through his designs intended to make working conditions as pleasant as possible, while at the same time producing a machine capable of tackling everything that could be reasonably expected of it.

The design was now at a stage where it was a relatively straightforward progression to the adoption of a three axle bogie with a corresponding increase in overall length. Beside better weight distribution this also allowed for a boiler and firebox of suitable size.

April 1946 produced the first of the 0-6-6-0 designs again with the provision for oil fueling.

But as has been shown before, Bulleid was seemingly unable to remain satisfied with anything for long. For this latest drawing contained a hint as to the possible inclusion of condensing apparatus to the 'Holcroft–Anderson' design. Somewhat suprising in view of the abortive tests carried out on the Southern using this system in 1930–5.

This first 0-6-6-0 was in reality a compromise. An engine with conventional piston valves, 4ft. 1in. wheels and a boiler pressure of 280 p.s.i., yet still with a water tube firebox. The inclusion of the third axle on each bogie meant the axle loading was reduced to an admirable 16.15T., although this had to be offset against the length of the monster, 62ft. 6in., similar to most coaches. This was especially so when contrasted against the M7 class maximum of 36ft. 3in., and even more so when seen as an M7 replacement working in and out of such a restricted layout as Waterloo.

Shortly afterwards Bulleid attended another of the regular meetings with the Traffic Manager. This time Richards raised the need for additional locomotives for use on the cross-London freight workings much of which were worked by the 'W' class tanks. Bulleid reportedly listened to the request in silence and then in an outburst so typical of the man proclaimed, '. . . you don't really want them, because they are confined to one class of duty. What you need is a substantially more powerful mixed traffic tank locomotive with full route availability.'

In practice this would not have been feasible, for if Bulleid had bothered to investigate further he would have found that at times five hours or more could be spent at Brent or Willesden waiting for the LMS yard staff to make up a train for the return journey. It was just not possible to diagram an engine for another duty elsewhere when such unpredictable timings were involved. As the fault was not of the Southerns' making there was little scope for possible improvement.

So why did Bulleid continue with what was already such a complicated design? The answer must lie in his own forceful character, his stubborn insistence that the continuation of development was not only desirable but essentially necessary for the future motive power requirements of the Southern Railway. How the directors ever came to sanction this further development of steam, especially in view of their publicly avowed policy towards electrification, must remain the subject of conjecture.

As with the earlier 'Merchant Navy's', Bulleid thus set himself the criteria and ideals his new locomotive should reach. 'An all round performer capable of handling passenger and goods trains normally taken by the West Country and Q1 class engines and able to reach speeds of 90 mph.' He went on to state that there should also be a reduction in the maintainance required. The last statement was one with which no doubt every locomotive designer would wish to concur. Indeed these ideals had already been displayed in certain aspects of his previous ventures but, as already recalled, in practice the reverse was often the case.

With assured confidence Bulleid next wrote to the General Manager;

> Sir Eustace Missenden, 11.7.1946
>
> In order to meet these requirements (referring to the original dictate of the Traffic Manager) within the limits imposed by the Chief Civil Engineer as regards permanent way and bridges. I propose a locomotive in accordance with the enclosed diagram. The engine will have a maximum speed of 90 mph and will be able to work goods trains which are normally taken by the Q1 and passenger trains equal to the 'West Country' engines, and will carry at least sufficient water and coal to run 80 miles between taking water and 150 miles without taking coal.
>
> The engine weights are so distributed as to enable it to run over the whole of the Company's lines with the following exceptions;
>
> Wenford Bridge line
> Hayling Island Branch
> Bere Alston and Callington
> Rye Harbour Branch
> Newhaven Swing Bridge
> Dover, Prince of Wales Pier
> Axminster and Lyme Regis Branch
> Isle of Wight lines
> – none of which is important
>
> It is estimated that, if a batch of 25 engines of this class were built, cost per engine would be £17,000. If one prototype was built, the cost would obviously be greater, dependant upon the development work found necessary during construction and might reach £25,000.'

It was now up to the directors to hopefully sanction approval. Bulleid used the time to continue on a number of variations to the drawings. Again the 0-6-6-0 concept was used but this time the wheelbase was lengthened so that a 70ft. turntable would have been required – at that time there were few of these on the Southern!

In addition a dry back boiler with thermic syphons was proposed whilst sleeve valves were shown to be incorporated.

The dry back boiler itself may be more correctly described as a conventional boiler attached to a firebox in which only the crown (or top) is covered by water. Both sides and back being of plain metal and again similar to the Paget engine. The thermic syphons were to assist in water circulation to and from the crown, two of which had already been incorporated in the Pacific firebox but allied to conventional principles. In the new design there would be no less than four syphons and so provide the maximum available surface space for heat transfer in what was the hottest part of the engine. In this way the resultant loss of heating surface due to the 'dry-sides' could be offset. It was a commendable effort and a major stage towards Bulleid's avowed aim of reduced maintainance. The inclusion of the dry sides compared with a conventional stayed firebox counterbalanced by no loss of firebox efficiency.

Bulleid took the first steps towards a patent for his new design on 2.9.46, but it was not until 21.1.49 that Patent No. 616.445 was issued covering 'Improvements relating to locomotive and like steam boilers.'

The inclusion of sleeve valves was a direct result of Hutchinson's drawings. A modification to the standard sleeve valve principle was also envisaged in that a degree of axial rotation was imparted during the stroke and intended to reduce the likelihood of seizure. (This modification was at the suggestion of Sir Harry Ricardo whose engineering company at Shoreham had conducted much research into the sleeve valve principle.)

Aesthetically the ends of the engine now took on a decidedly rounded appearance, not unlike the Pacifics which in turn were similar to contemporary French styling. In part this was due to the increased front overhang dictated by the use of sleeve valves which were in themselves relatively long and thin. The overall length was shown as no less than 66ft.

With new ideas flowing on an almost daily basis one can almost imagine Bulleid impatiently awaiting final authorisation to proceed. This came one step closer on 4 September when a meeting of 'The Rolling Stock (Repair and Renewals) Progress Committee' was held at Waterloo. The latest drawings were made available to the meeting along with a descriptive memo from the C.M.E. himself.

LEADING CLASS. SHUNTING ENGINE. C-C TYPE

The principle features of the new engine are as follows;

This design of engine makes full and complete use of the total weight for adhesive purposes and braking. The type of bogie is similar to that introduced on the electric locomotive, the riding of which has been found to be satisfactory. The springs and gear will be above the axleboxes and under continuous lubrication. The whole of the moving parts will be enclosed and fitted with automatic lubrication, so that it will not be necessary for the driver to lubricate any part of the machine. Each engine will have three 'simple' cylinders driving the intermediate axle. The load is transmitted to the leading and trailing axles by chain drive in an oiltight casing. Roller bearing boxes will be fitted to all axles and will receive force feed lubrication. The axleboxes will be contained in an oilbath. Each axlebox guide is fitted with a 'Silentbloc' bearing. The leading engine will exhaust to atmosphere, by way of the blast pipe in the smokebox, so as to provide the necessary draught in the boiler, but exhaust from the trailing engine will be used to heat the water in the tank, the hot water being pumped to the boiler by suitable hot water pumps. The boiler is a new design which will obviate the maintainance inherent in the normal type of locomotive boiler. The engine will also be fitted with feed water treatment incorporated in the tender. The controls of the engine will be such that both men will be able to carry out their duties seated and will be duplicated where necessary, so that they can drive in either direction. The weight of water and fuel indicated should be ample for the normal requirements of the Southern Railway, especially as by condensing steam from one engine, the water consumption should be appreciably reduced. The engine is fitted with 5ft. 1in. wheels and this in conjunction with the short stroke, will allow the engine to run at speeds up to 90 mph, without exceeding the normal piston speed. The engine will not be air-smoothed in any sense of the word, but the

> front end will be based on that sucessfully introduced on the 'West Country' class engines, in order to ensure that the steam, when the engine is working lightly, is carried clear of the cab.

This was the first time the project had been officially referred to as the 'Leading Class', possibly the idea of the Public Relations Department, but from it of course came the connotation 'Leader'. Mention is also made of 'simple' cylinders and this ought perhaps to be explained in the light of the previous references to sleeve valves. Simple cylinders refer to the use of steam for expansion once only before exhausting to the blast pipe or pre-heating the feed. It matters not as to the design of valves used to control the entry and exit of the steam into the cylinders and indeed over the years a number of different types had been used in the steam locomotive.

Another anomaly relates to the statement that both the crew would be able to perform their duties seated. As far as this refers to the driver it is easy to explain, but hand-firing a locomotive from a seated position is impossible for any length of time. It is all the more difficult to explain as by this time all references to oil firing are missing from the drawings whilst there is similarly no reference to mechanical stoking.

Finally the mention of feed pumps and pre-heating, which was a far from new idea. In this way overall efficiency was raised but at the expense of added mechanical complications and in a country where water is a plentiful commodity it is unlikely any worthwhile savings could be accrued. Possibly though Bulleid hoped to carry less water, and use what was carried in a more efficient way so saving on weight. (2500 gallons of water weighs approx 11.5 tons.) But whatever the reason the proposal was dropped. It is the opinion of the author that this was possibly partly due to a desire to incorporate T.I.A. water treatment which would be upset by the presence of particles of lubricating oil in the condensed water.

To the frustration of the C.M.E. no immediate decision was given to proceed, although it was minuted that '. . . an early decision was desirable.' This was in no small part due to a representative of the Superintendent of Operations Department arguing with some passion against the prospect of some twenty five new machines which comprised so many ' . . . unorthodox and untried ideas', and suggesting instead that trials be carried out with only one prototype. Conservatism or knowledgeable caution?

Bulleid, however, was not to be so easily put off and continued in his attempt to push through his ideas. Most of the committee were also non-technical and he used this to advantage. An understandable compromise was then reached, five engines were to be built. Hardly satisfactory to the Traffic Manager who still awaited his replacement for the M7's.

The following day confirmation of the decision arrived.

> From the General Manager;
> To the Chief Mechanical Engineer.
>
> PROPOSED TANK ENGINE
>
> With reference to Minute 79 of the meeting of the Progress Committee held yesterday, the Traffic Manager informs me that he has had a further discussion with you upon this matter and he now recommends we proceed with the building of five engines to diagram W7326. I shall be glad if you will proceed accordingly.'

Boiler Pressure – 280lbs per sq. in.
Cylinders – 13¼ in. Dia. × 15 in. stroke
Tractive Effort at 85% B.P. – 30,800 lbs
Adhesion Factor – 7.28

'LEADER' CLASS
TYPE C.C.

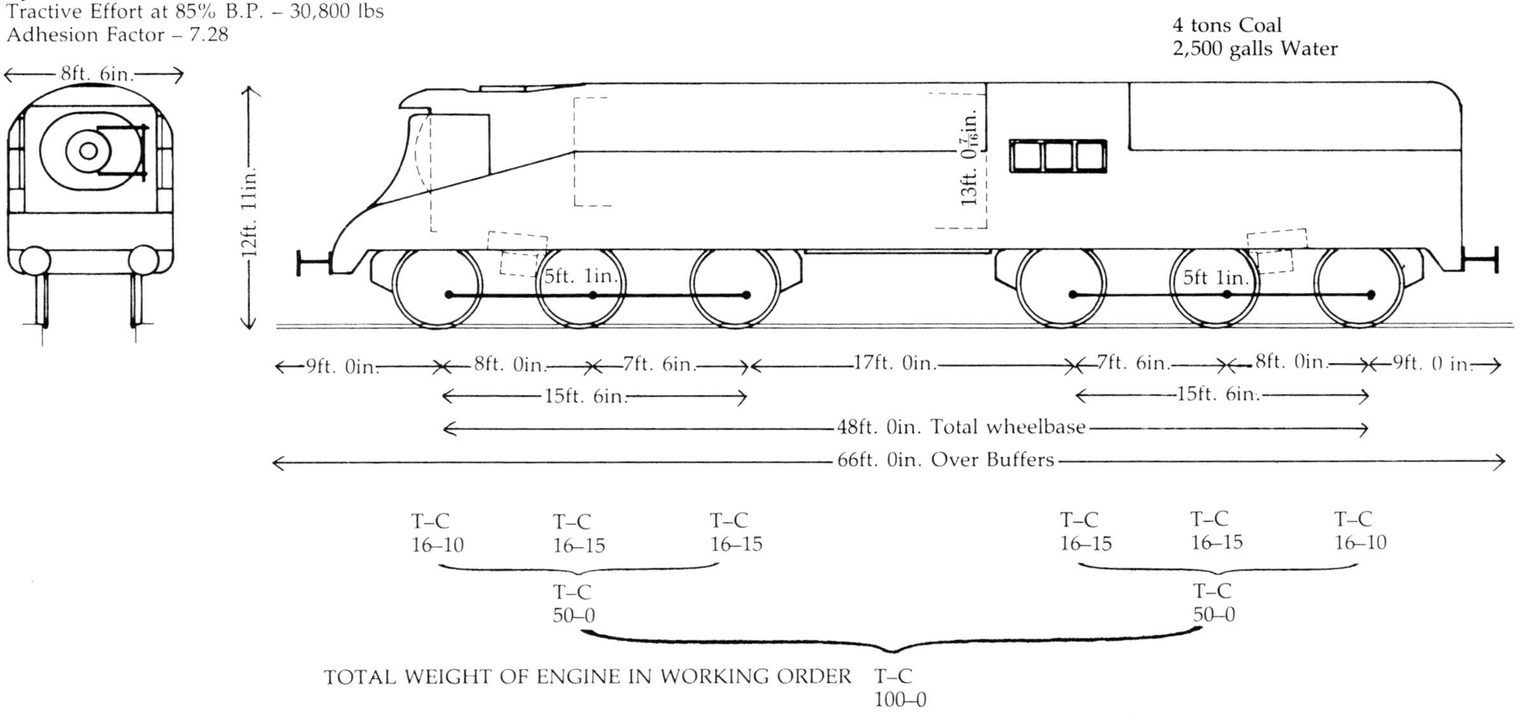

Presumably the further discussion referred to between Bulleid and Richards centred around the latters' apprehension of likely teething troubles to come.

Matters now progressed rapidly, with an official order, No. 3382 issued to the Brighton Drawing Office on 11.9.46, that simply stated 'Build five tank engines to Diagram W7326.'

Thus there began to emerge the first of hundreds of separate drawings necessary for the new design. Several have survived and are dated either 1946 or 1947 but are unlikely to be of much interest at the present time as they just cover the basic engineering details of the new design.

In the meantime the administrative process ground on with the Traffic Manager submitting his official requirements for the new design to the R.S. (Repair & Renewals) P.C. at Waterloo at the beginning of October.

> 'In reply to your letter of the 5th. September and referring to minute No 79 of the Progress Committee Meeting held on the 4th September. The case justifying the construction of 25 new passenger tank engines is given below. At the present time and, indeed, for the past 45 years the most powerful passenger tank engines on the Western Section have been those of the M7 class, 104 of which are still in existence. These engines were built between the years 1897–1911 and although the last 49 embody slight improvements, the whole class was based on a design prepared in 1897 and now, therefore, nearly 50 years old. They were originally built for L & SWR suburban traffic and were, in due course, rendered redundant by electrification. They are now being used as general utility locomotives, 25% working empty trains between Clapham Junction, or other stock berthing points and Waterloo, and the balance on local and branch line services on the Western Section. They are completely out of date and inefficient by modern standards, and their continued existence prevents any improvement on the services they operate. In the report to yourself dated 1.12.1944, upon our locomotive position in 1950, prepared by the Deputy General Manager and other Chief Officers, the whole of these 104 engines were condemned, and this recommendation was confirmed in the corresponding report upon the 1955 locomotive position submitted on 3.9.1946. The report dealing with the Engine Building Programme during the years 1947–1955 recommends the building of 60 new tank engines, diesel or steam, in addition to the 25 tanks already proposed, and I now recommend that the latter be constructed. It is understood that the five engines to be built will be a guide as to the building of the subsequent 20.'
>
> (Unfortunately the reports referred to above concerning the locomotive position in 1950 and 1955 have not been traced.)

So why had such a shortage of suitable steam power been allowed to occur? It is not necessary to look far to find the answer – a preoccupation with electrification at the expense of steam.

Meanwhile at a board meeting on 3.10.46 an interesting comment arises;

> 'Mr. Bulleid also said that only one of the new Passenger Tanks would

be completed in June 1947, and that the remaining four would follow as soon as possible thereafter.
The Traffic Manager intimated that from an operating point of view it would be better if the five engines were constructed for coal burning in order to ensure greater mobility, particularly in regard to Depot allocation, and the Chairman requested the Chief Mechanical Engineer to proceed accordingly.'

The opportunity for 'Leader' to be oil fired had been lost, it was the first of many pitfalls that eventually led to the failure of the engine. Certainly matters could perhaps have been rectified had a mechanical stoker been fitted, but no plans to suggest this have been found. It is also worth pointing out that this was at a time when the Government of the day had entered into a commitment for the use of oil fuel on railway locomotives. But to digress further on that particular topic is to become involved in the political arena of the day and it is now time to return again to October 1946 and the further progression of the design.

To the staff of the C.M.E.'s department this was an exciting time, their railway was involved in research into the ultimate steam engine, potentially the most exciting development for decades. But such euphoria was not necessarily universal, for a number of senior staff still expressed a degree of scepticism, fuelled by the fact that the existing Pacific engines spent a considerable amount of time in the works undergoing one modification after another.

Bulleid though was far from restrained and apparently heedless to both the criticism of his Pacific's and calls for caution over 'Leader'. Consequently he pushed ahead and now included as an essential criteria the advantages of a driving cab at each end, so alleviating the need for a turntable at terminal stations.

Accordingly a design was prepared which showed a driving cab at each end but in addition having a corridor connection as well. One is tempted to ask the obvious question, what would this have been for? Surely not as the LNER practice of crew changing en route, as on the Southern even the longest runs were too short a distance to warrant this? Could it possibly have been the first suggestion towards multiple working?

Another feature not shown clearly was the central firing compartment and if it was to have windows on both sides. Nor how the balance was to be restored from placing the boiler offset from the centre line. This last modification would allow access between all three cabs via a narrow corridor. Indeed only a few months later when a senior Brighton Official was asked, 'How are you going to balance the offset boiler?' The reply received was, '. . . that is a good question, we are still trying to discover the answer!' Evidently it was never forthcoming.

Meanwhile at the Brighton drawing office there was feverish activity, although outside the confines of the works little was known. Understandably rumours were rife, these sometimes provoking the comment that the footplate crews would object to working in enforced solitude. Presumably none of these critics had recourse to consider the existing push–pull arrangements or single manning of electric units.

Then in December 1946 the first orders for material were placed with various outside suppliers. It was also realised that the project was now not only a challange to technical advancement but also a race against time with nationalisation just one year away.

Accordingly, with the drawing office working flat out, the final designs for the sleeve valves were ready in the spring of 1947, while at the same time the advantages of an all welded construction were being investigated. But as already stated, other than in the Paget engine, sleeve valves had had little railway use and so it was wisely decided to convert an existing engine as a 'guinea pig' for the new venture. Eventually an 'H1' – Atlantic was chosen. (See next chapter.)

Bulleid made what was probably the first reference to the 'Leader' project outside the works in June 1947 when he lectured at the Centenary of the Institution of Mechanical Engineers. Referring to the potential advantages of the new design he stated;

> 'A new type of heavy, mixed traffic tank engine is under construction and these engines embody further developments of the innovations introduced in the tender engines, all with the object of developing a steam engine as easy to maintain and operate as possible. As the locomotive is carried on two six-wheeled bogies, the whole weight is available for adhesion and braking and the engine can run over 97 percent of the company's system.'

Bulleid was however, slightly ahead of himself here, simply because construction did not actually start at Brighton until July 1947. The former LBSCR works was used as it was the only one of the three SR workshops with spare capacity for such a project. There were other advantages in using Brighton, for here was the C.M.E.'s head office whilst the works drawing office was responsible for most of the detail drawings.

A more public mention was made concerning the project on 18.10.47 as part of an address Bullied gave to the Institute of Mechanical Engineers, to which body he had recently been elected president. Eight days later an abstract of the paper was published in the journal *Modern Transport* under the title 'New Conception of Steam Locomotive Design – Lessons for the Immediate Future'. An extract from this is shown in Appendix C and clearly shows the character of the designer together with his intentions.

Understandably there was a great deal of interest shown in Bulleid's paper and such enthusiasm was relished within the C.M.E.'s department. This in turn encouraged the flow of ideas, including an interchangable power bogie, another of the inherent advantages of the diesel/electric lobby, although on financial grounds alone a fleet far greater than five engines would have been needed to justify holding spares.

But practical progress was slow with the first set of main frames not completed until May 1948, five months into nationalisation. Indeed throughout the project it would be fair to say certain work was completed on an *ad hoc* basis and apparently without the benefit of drawings, these were either not available or almost impossible to comprehend after numerous amendments.

In the meantime thirty-one more engines to the same design had been authorised in November 1947. But this was purely a pre-nationalisation gesture by the Southern Railway for the order was never confirmed by the Railway Executive.

It was also a close run thing that the original order for just five engines was allowed to proceed, especially as work was nowhere near completion. Indeed questions were already being asked both at Waterloo and 222 Marylebone Road – Headquarters of the Railway Executive, concerning the cost of the project. This was quoted in July 1948 as £87,500 for five engines, subsequently adjusted by the Chief Accountant just two months later to £100,000. These figures were approximately double the cost of constructing a comparatively powered steam locomotive to an existing design. With money short it was understandable that the project became known as 'Bleeder' when reference was made to the escalating costs. One official when asked if he was worried over the finance replied, '. . . worried is not the word.'

Through all the turmoil created by nationalisation Bulleid had been allowed to remain in charge of the project. His ally the former SR General Manager, Sir Eustace Missenden had been elevated to Chairman of the Railway Executive, with the new boss at Waterloo, Sir John Elliot equally sympathetic. But overall charge of mechanical engineering on BR came now under the control of Robin Riddles at Marylebone, and while there was never any question of personal animosity between Bulleid and his senior colleagues, Riddles knew enough of Bulleid to keep a wary eye on his activities.

Had work continued under a private Southern Railway the engine numbering would have been to Bulleid's unusual style, CC101-5, with names likely to have included:

Missenden, Sir Eustace
Churchill, Sir Winston
Montgomery, Field Marshal
Walker, Sir Hubert

In the event BR allocated Nos. 36001–5 with no vestige of names. As far as is known nameplates were never cast.

Pressure was also being brought to bear to have the engines completed, and so the decision was taken to concentrate resources on the first of the class temporarily at the expense of the remainder. Ironically this meant work pressed ahead on No. 36001 before any necessary lessons learnt from the trials of the converted 'H1' could be incorporated.

Consequently No. 36001 steamed away from Brighton for the first time in late June 1949, two years late and even then still incomplete, as Brighton had complained of difficulties in fitting the multiple valve rings. Bulleid impatiently decided Eastleigh could complete the work.

Much else was different from diagram W7326 of 1946 and on which the approval to go ahead had been based. The offset boiler, position of driving cabs and outer casing are just three examples. The concept of the corridor connections had also disappeared whilst the suggested cowlings at the ends had not materialised. Three windows at each end provided for an uninterupted view of the way ahead.

But what was the way ahead, and where would it lead? Towards a resurgence for steam or the seemingly remorseless march onward of the diesels? Now was the time to watch and ponder on the days ahead.

THE PRELUDE

The experimental engines and *Hartland Point*

With work progressing on No. 36001 at Brighton the opportunity was taken to assess the suitability of some of the features it was hoped to incorporate within the new design.

The first of these involved the fitting of a 'U1' class 2-6-0 No. 1896 with a 6in. square duct in the base of the smokebox through which char and ash could drop to the track. This it was hoped would reduce the problem of the engine smokebox becoming choked with cinders after hard working for some distance and its consequently detrimental effect on steaming.

The first experiment, 'U1' No. 1896 fresh from overhaul at Ashford Works in the summer of 1946 and probably at the time the open ash duct was fitted. How such a fitment was physically routed around the centre cylinder of this three cylinder engine is not clear. Almost certainly the ash chute would have been under some form of remote control from the driver, for otherwise with the chute permanently open steaming would have been seriously impaired.

R.C. Riley

Of course if the oil firing of 'Leader' had ever been a serious consideration, such fitments would have been rendered unnecessary. But on the 'Leader' design as it stood the experiment was of considerable importance, for the disposal of hot ash from an enclosed smokebox was rightly recognised as not only an unpleasant but also a potentially dangerous task and certainly one to be avoided if at all possible. There must have been considerable satisfaction then that No. 1896 performed reasonably well, although she was fresh from overhaul.

While this particular experiment may have been new, the same could not be said of the desire to develop a self-cleaning type of smokebox. Indeed many years earlier, J.G. Robinson, as C.M.E. of the Great Central used a series of steam jets within the smokebox which were under the remote control of the driver. Their function was to stir up the ash and direct it upwards into the blast from which it dispersed out of the chimney. This took place at intervals along the journey and consequently when travelling in GCR trains it was common to hear 'hail-stones' on the carriage roof coinciding with the ejection of ashes. An unfortunate side effect was that the legal department of the railway were kept busy with claims where hot cinders were alledgedly responsible for setting fire to property alongside the railway! As the GCR had been absorbed into his former employers, the LNER in 1923, Bulleid would no doubt have been aware of this early work.

Already one question arises, why did Bulleid start these experiments when some years earlier the LNER had fitted the same type of open duct in the smokebox and which

A self-cleaning smokebox on a former GWR 'King' class engine photographed at Swindon during BR days. The mesh screens were removable so as to afford access to the tubes and blastpipe. Similar screens were fitted by BR to a number of engines from 1951 onwards.

'R.A.' Collection

had already been proven to be a failure. The problem being that despite the duct supposedly being able to be closed by remote action from the cab, ash and char would prevent a secure fit and consequently air continued to be drawn into the usual vacuum of the smokebox and thereby impaired steaming.

Ironically a few years later BR were to fit fine mesh screens within the smokebox of a number of engines and with considerable success. These performed the task of preventing the char from falling to the floor, being caught instead in the blast before being successfully ejected from the chimney.

HARTLAND POINT

As previously referred to briefly, it was decided to test the proposed sleeve valve principle in service and the search began for a suitable guinea pig engine. This was after a preliminary quarter scale model of the adapted Bulleid valve gear associated with sleeve valves was made and which gave good valve event timing.

The C.M.E.'s department eventually selected a Marsh Atlantic of the 'H1' class for the trials. No. 2039 *Hartland Point* was taken into Brighton works in July 1947. The choice of this engine is particularly interesting, for it is alleged that the first preference had been that of a 'King Arthur' class locomotive. But the use of one of these machines allied to the new cylinders dictated by the inclusion of sleeve valves, and coupled to the same size pistons as before, would have fouled the loading gauge. There would have been no reason why smaller pistons could not have been used, although it has also been suggested that the Motive Power Department were reluctant at the thought of giving up what was a reliable straight-forward engine.

No. 454 *Queen Guinevere* of the King Arthur class portrayed outside Exmouth Junction shed. Despite a member of this class being ruled out for conversion to sleeve valves, Bulleid did successfully modify many of the type with a multiple jet blast pipe and wide diameter chimney. No. 454 is shown before any such modification and also displays to advantage the high standard of external cleanliness once commonplace on the railways.

Lens of Sutton

There were five engines in the H1 class, built as Nos. 37–41 by Messrs Kitson between December 1905 and February 1906; their ancestry from the design of the earlier Great Northern Atlantics is clearly discernable. No. 39 is shown in almost original condition complete with bogie brakes which were later removed. When selected for conversion by Bulleid there were strong views over the choice of this particular machine. One being that sister engine No. 2037 should have been selected as she was always a shy steamer. Nos. 2038 and 2039 were seen as the best of the class and by converting one it was regarded as a waste of a good engine.
Collection of Les Warnett

The Atlantic however was on the short list for scrapping. Certainly with time at a premium the choice of 2039 was no doubt based on the simplicity of the original design, although it is also interesting to reflect that one of Bulleid's existing types was not selected.

Accordingly with No. 2039 due for withdrawal the decision was made to sacrifice piston diameter for compatability within the loading gauge. As a result the actual piston size was reduced from 19in. to 14in., although the stroke remained constant at 26 in. with the crankpins unaltered. This meant that with the 6ft. 7in. wheels fitted the nominal tractive effort was reduced from 20,070lbs to 11,892lbs – assessed at 85% b.p.

MECHANICAL WORK

Work on the conversion involved an almost complete rebuild of the front end. As apart from the new cylinders a multiple jet blast pipe was fitted together with the well known Bulleid large diameter chimney. The Westinghouse air pump was also resited to the right hand side of the smokebox.

For both ease and quickness of manufacture the outer casing of the new cylinders was in the form of a fabricated steel shell. Around the outside was welded a central 'live' steam annulus, flanked by an exhaust steam annulus at either end. A cast 'Mechanite' (fine grain cast iron) liner was pressed into the cylinder to provide a working bearing surface for the sleeve valve which was itself basically a partial tube of Mechanite. The actual sleeve was machined to a sliding fit and sealed with 30 separate rings.

No. 2039 during the course of conversion in Brighton Works. This is the right hand cylinder, although yet to be attached are the connections from the sleeve lugs to the oscillating gear. Note the running plate has been removed from behind the cylinder as far as the buffer beam. A number of components including the new bogie are yet to be added.
National Railway Museum

The machined inside diameter of the sleeve formed a cylinder in which a normal type of piston worked. At either end separate steam and exhaust ports were machined around the periphery of both sleeve and liner and so allowed steam to travel between the respective annulus and cylinder proper.

Each sleeve was provided with two integrally cast extension lugs which protruded through the front cylinder cover. These were bridged by a machined steel cross-bar bolted between each lug. Steam was admitted to each cylinder via a central joint on the top face of the cylinder and to which a short length of round steel tube, set inward, provided the connection to prefabricated protrusions welded to the outside walls of the circular smokebox. Although not aesthetically pleasing it was probably the most practical method, after all *Hartland Point* was essentially a mobile test bed. Two exhaust connections were made by equally practical if ugly means.

The increase in overall length of the new cylinders meant the existing 3ft. 6in. diameter bogie wheels were fouled. This was overcome by substituting the bogie with one from a 'D3' 0-4-4 tank with 3ft. wheels.

The valve events were controlled as before by an internal Stephenson's link motion. The valve rods were connected to plungers and guide bushes pressed into a fabricated steel stretcher bolted between the frames. This stretcher was itself in the space originally occupied by the inside steam chests.

To transmit the drive to the outside of the frames, a rocking lever was mounted either side, each pivoted in a substantial bushed steel housing bolted to the outside face of the frame. The outer links drove rearwards and were attached to each of the sleeve cross-bars where connection was made by universal ball-type joints. This was to absorb the independant oscillating drive. The latter was itself obtained from a rotating camshaft sprocket driven by a 'Morse' inverted tooth chain from the leading coupled axle.

Right hand cylinder and sleeve showing the connections to the oscillating gear from the extended sleeve 'ears'. In the top right corner one of the two mechanical lubricators is visible, although the position of both of these beneath the smokebox door was far from ideal. This location of course was subject to a liberal covering of ash and cinders every time the smokebox was cleaned. The mass of exposed oil pipes is only too apparent, the whole appearance typifying the engine as an experimental venture.

Derek Clayton

The shaft was mounted in bearings located on both main frames, through which they protruded to terminate with an eccentric flange on either end. The flange worked in a horizontal slot provided in a bearing block bolted to the outside radius of the inner sleeve lub. Thus as the sleeve was made to reciprocate and so provide the valve events, an oscillating motion was imparted to facilitate lubrication and even out wear. The sleeve performed a 'figure of eight' movement which was reputedly fascinating to watch.

THE WHY AND THE WHEREFORE

Bulleid's object in employing a sleeve valve cylinder design was to obtain a marked increase in thermal efficiency. Theoretically this would certainly be higher than that procured from a conventional slide or piston valve engine as with sleeve valves the cylinders would suffer less condensation. This was because the steam and exhaust annulia would keep the cylinder temperature both higher and more constant during each stroke. A large steam chest (or steam charge) volume of 3¼ times the cylinder volume at maximum cut-off would also result from the large steam admission annuli. Increased steam flow could then be expected, similar facilities allowed for a free flowing exhaust.

However loss of mechanical efficiency had to be offset against the improved thermal advantages. This was due to the high frictional losses attributed to maintaining a steam tight seal across the exhaust ports and the front radial outlet slots for the extension drive lugs.

In an attempt to reduce this to a minimum a large number of oil feed connections were made along the upper faces of the cylinders. Accordingly generous pressure lubrication was available to the large bearing surfaces and multitude of sealing rings on the sleeves. Two 'Wakefield' mechanical lubricators, chain driven, were mounted between the frames ahead of the smokebox and pumped oil via a network of copper pipes and connectors.

With the need for accessibility whilst undergoing trials, together with the difficulty of fitting the running plates around the top entry steam and exhaust connections, the running plates were terminated at the rear end of the cylinders. Together with the mass of exposed pipes and oil feeds this feature did much to alter the previously graceful outline of the original Marsh design.

THE TESTS WITH No. 2039

Unlike the later runs with 'Leader', the trials of No. 2039 are referred to only briefly in official records and consequently it is not certain that a full record of all runs and tests was compiled.

What is believed to have been the first steaming of the modified engine took place on 5.11.47, although this was probably only a preliminary shop test. At this stage no rings had been fitted to the sleeves so there was considerable steam leakage from the front end. Following this came a series of works tests, one on 3.12.47 witnessed by Bulleid's brother-in-law, H.G. Ivatt, where the engine was reported as running well but still shrouded in escaping steam from the front end.

No. 2039 then re-entered the works for the fitting of the necessary piston rings, following which on 15.12.47 she was noted in steam, first outside the works and then later the same day at the nearby Brighton running shed. The same afternoon a trip was made to Lewes in company with 'E5' tank No. 2404, the operating authorities obviously taking no chances of failure with a new and untried design. A short visit was then necessary to the works to replace a number of broken rings, while before the end of December some further tests were again made to Lewes.

The first day of the new year in 1948, and coincidently the first day of nationalised ownership of the railways, found No. 2039 working between Brighton and Eastbourne on empty stock formed with ex-SECR 3-car set No. 597. Although not carrying passengers, the train made a brief halt at each of the stations en route, the purpose of which was to gauge the acceleration characteristics of the engine in its modified form. Evidently all was well for there followed daily tests from Brighton to Groombridge via Lewes, a distance of some 30 miles. It was said on these duties the engine was very free running and reached a reputed 70–80 mph with ease.

In addition there were a number of light engine runs, mainly to Three Bridges, one at least with a 'K' class mogul being propelled in both directions.

It would certainly seem that results from these early trials were promising, for in February 1948, No. 2039 appeared at Eastleigh on an empty stock train from the carriage works at Lancing. Several further runs between Eastleigh and Lancing followed, in this way at least No. 2039 performed a useful role to the traffic department. By the end of the month though the engine was again back at Brighton and receiving attention in the works.

Between March and June 1948 there were a series of runs from Brighton to either Lewes or Cowden. Also in June a 3-coach set was worked between Brighton and Tunbridge Wells West and return, after which the destination was changed to Hastings, but still with the same trailing load. The series of tests concluded with a twice daily run at the head of a 4–5 coach set again to Tunbridge Wells which lasted sometime into July.

No. 2039 leaving Brighton for Groombridge on a test train. Trials were usually commenced from the passenger station so as to simulate as near as possible realistic working. In this way it was also possible to afford a direct comparison in running times.
P. Ransom Wallis/National Railway Museum

Details for the next couple of months are obscure but in September 1948, No. 2039 was seen at the head of a train of bogie utility vans after which the engine once more re-entered the works.

She was not to emerge again until early December 1948, and now on a series of light engine trials on the coast line as far as Hastings. Two trips were made each way and mainly at weekends. Perhaps because of previous successes, 19.12.48 saw the engine at the head of an Officers special from Ashford to Brighton. Unfortunately on leaving St. Leonards disaster struck with a sudden fracture of the right hand valve rod. The motion had to be taken down in the nearby shed yard followed by an ignominious tow back to Brighton.

No. 2039's next known outing was on 14.3.49, the Motive Power Department seemingly having enough faith to entrust the engine to a public passenger train. However, in view of the lack of use in the previous three months, it was more likely to be pressure exerted from other quarters that prompted such movement. Whatever the reasons No. 2039 was set to take the three coaches of the Hastings–Birkenhead through service between Brighton and Redhill, the task being accomplished without difficulty. The return working was also successfully achieved later the same day.

Two days later the engine was rostered for a further trip to Redhill, but this time on three empty coaches from Brighton. All was well until Earlswood was reached, just short of her destination, where No. 2039 was to totally disgrace herself. Apparently the free running capabilities and light load had resulted in an earlier than anticipated arrival

No. 2039 at Uckfield, again on a test working. Unlike 'Leader' it is not believed the reciprocating mechanism of the sleeves was ever removed. The lack of a headcode of any sort is obvious.
P. Ransom Wallis/National Railway Museum

so a signal check was encountered. The problem came when the signal cleared, the engine refusing to start, moving neither forward or back. It later transpired that the steam ports around the sleeve were inaccurately placed, although it is not clear if this was due to a fault in design, manufacture or setting.

While the crew struggled valiantly to persuade No. 2039 to move a pilot engine was urgently sought, and after 25 minutes the complete failure was hauled the short distance to Redhill. The return to Brighton later in the day was in company with 'E' class 4-4-0 No. 31587.

As previously recounted there is little background information available showing known modifications and repairs, so one can only speculate on any repairs that must have been carried out. But work there certainly was, for on 1.4.49, No. 2039 again ventured out at the head of a 3-coach special to Ashford. It was soon apparent that there were still difficulties, for following a signal stop at Ore it took 7½ minutes to restart, somewhat unfortunate as both Bulleid and a member of his senior staff were present on the footplate. Perhaps a more suitable day should have chosen for the test!

Whatever the impression gained it was not enough to prevent further runs, as a short time later No. 2039 was again at the head of a works train between Lancing and Eastleigh.

The original intention had been to return No. 2039 to her original form as soon as No. 36001 was completed, but this was never done, no doubt because of her anticipated short future life. Accordingly following a period of open store at Brighton she entered the works on 14.6.49. The focus of attention now transferred away from No. 2039 towards 'Leader' herself who was rapidly nearing completion.

A broken sleeve extracted from No. 2039 possibly following the failure at St. Leonards on 19.12.48. The number of runs made light engine indicate the varying degrees of success associated with the trials. The discolouration along part of the length of the sleeve is an indication of seizure, possibly caused by lack of adequate lubrication, which may well have contributed to this particular failure.
National Railway Museum

No. 2039 languished for most of the summer within the works, perhaps awaiting a decision as to her future. Eventually the choice was made and amidst a degree of surprise she was given a 'heavy intermediate' overhaul which even included fitting a replacement boiler sent especially from Eastleigh. The engine emerged from Brighton as BR No. 32039 *Hartland Point* on 3.9.49 still with the sleeve valves and she was allocated to Brighton shed shortly afterwards.

There now followed a period of some 16 months during which any movements of the engine are not clear. Possibly much of this time was spent in store although the economic sense of this following an expensive overhaul are open to question.

Drawing purely on what would seem to be likely and is therefore conjecture, it must be said that No. 32039 was not in a reliable enough condition to work in normal traffic. The engine was considerably less powerful than others of her type and the retention of the sleeve valves meant her reputation was still open to question. Accordingly with all eyes focussed on No. 36001, *Hartland Point* was quietly laid aside, we shall never know if her perfomance had improved following the overhaul.

This lack of documentary data on any trials of No. 2039 make conclusions hard to effect. What is recalled with certainty is No. 2039's prolific water consumption, for when working between Lancing and Eastleigh stops had to be made at Chichester and Fareham to replenish the tender. Purely on a mileage basis alone this represents a figure of 87 gall/mile or a 350% increase on what could normally be expected. Much of this was certainly due to the continued breaking of rings; indeed upon routine piston examination most of the rings would be found to be already broken or at the very least cracked. It was never firmly established if this was a design or assembly fault. Consequently when running the front of the loco would be enveloped in steam.

In store outside Brighton Works. It would appear long periods were spent out of use in this way although when she did run it was with any crew that was available and unlike 'Leader' not the responsibility of just a single set of men. The name *Hartland Point* continued to be carried up to the time of eventual withdrawal.

W.H.G. Boot (courtesy N.E. Stead)

Hartland Point in steam at Eastleigh following a trip with carriage underframes from Lancing. Of the three pipes above the cylinders the outer two are for the exhaust and the centre pipe for the steam input from the regulator valve.

S.C. Townroe

Fresh after overhaul in September 1949 and now numbered 32039. Compared with previous views it can be seen that the snifting valves have at some stage been removed from the smokebox casing, possibly when the replacement boiler was fitted. The tender is without any form of ownership and remained as such until condemned along with the engine.

'R.A.' Collection

By February 1951 the end had at last come and a directive was received from Headquarters to move the engine to Eastleigh for assessment. She was found to be unsuitable to make the trip under her own power, probably because of the protracted time spent in store. Accordingly No. 32039 was towed from Brighton by 'C2X' No. 32438. At Eastleigh the final decision was made and after a further brief period in store she was finally cut up.

No. 32039's demise cannot be other than expected. By 1951 she was surplus to requirements, an odd-ball not worthy of maintaining, especially as the design she had pre-determined was already condemned. Her failings as a guinea pig were surely only haste in design for she had at least proved the sleeve valve concept was worthy of further development. It was not through any fault of No. 2039 that 'Leader' failed to accede to her designers wishes. Unfortunately no direct comparative trials or dynamometer car tests were ever carried out with No. 2039 although it is unlikely these could have prolonged her life. She had at least proven the way, even if before 'Leader' ever turned a wheel it was clear there was still a long way to go.

With no useful life left *Hartland Point* was towed to Eastleigh from Brighton on 17.2.51 and photographed a week later on the day she was officially withdrawn. Four weeks later she was again under tow the short distance to the nearby works where she was finally cut up.

Les Elsey

CHRONOLOGY OF No. 2039

December 1905 – February 1906	Built by Kitson & Co. Given the number '39' by the LBSCR.
October 1908	Steam heating fitted.
June 1913	Named *La France.*
January 1926	Renumbered and renamed by the SR. Now No. 2039 *Hartland Point.*
July 1947	To Brighton Works for conversion as mobile test bed for sleeve valve experiments.
5.11.47	Ex-works from Brighton.
3.12.47	Yard trial at Brighton. Bulleid and Ivatt present.
December 1947	Works visits and trial Brighton–Lewes.
15.12.47	To Lewes in company with No. 2404.
1.1.48	Worked 3-coach set Brighton–Eastbourne.
January 1948	Daily test train Brighton–Groombridge via Lewes. Light engine runs Brighton–Three Bridges. 'K' Class 2-6-0 propelled to Three Bridges and return.
February 1948	Works visit. Trip(s) to Eastleigh. Works visit.
Mar–Jun 1948	Test train on coastway line Brighton to Lewes or Cowden. 3-coach set Brighton to Tunbridge Wells West and return, or same load to Hastings and return.
July–Aug 1948	Works visits?
September 1948	Train of bogie utility vans. To works.
December 1948	Light engine trials to Hastings. Failed at St. Leonards with broken valve rod on 19.12.48.
Jan–Feb 1949	Works. Trials?
14.3.49	First public passenger train Brighton to Redhill and return.
16.3.49	Trial run with 3 coaches Brighton to Redhill, failed at Earlswood.
Apr–Jun 1949	Special to Ashford with Bulleid on footplate. Stock trains Lancing to Eastleigh. Works visits and storage.
14.6.49–3.9.49	Brighton Works. Overhaul.
Sept 1949 – Feb 1951	Stored at Brighton?
17.2.51	Towed from Brighton to Eastleigh.
24.2.51	Withdrawn from Eastleigh.
March 1951	Scrapped at Eastleigh Works.

IN 14.6.49 OUT 3.9.49 1026 H/Intermediate

32039 Changed Boiler. Steam pipes remd, repd & refitted. Cylinder relief valves remd, repd & refitted. Cylinder cock gear remd, replaced. Blast pipe remd, cleaned & refitted. Crossheads remd, repd & refitted. Eccentric rods remd & replaced. Connecting rods & coupling rods remd, repd & refitted. Engine & Tender uncoupled & recoupled. Blower pipe remd, repd & refitted. Chimney remd & refitted. Inter drawbar remd repd & refitted. Damper gear remd, repd & refitted. W.H. & Vacuum Ejector pipes remd, repd & refitted. Firehole door remd repd & refitted. Pressure gauges (5) remd, repd & refitted. Guard Irons remd repd & refitted. Horn stays & check plates remd, repd & refitted. Handrails & pillars remd & replaced. Injector gear remd, repd & refitted. S.F. Lubricator remd & replaced. Lagging remd, repd & refitted. Cellboxes remd, repd & replaced. Reversing gear remd & replaced. Reservoirs remd, repd & replaced. Splashers remd, repd & refitted. Sandboxes remd & replaced. Sander gear & stays remd, repd & refitted. Vacuum Ejector remd, repd & refitted. W.H. Brake valve remd, repd & refitted. Whistle gear remd & replaced. Watering & Ashpan Cocks remd & replaced. C.I. number plate fitted to smokebox door. Frame stretchers remd & replaced. Driving Chain remd replaced. Axleboxes remd repd & refitted. Wheels remd & replaced. Tyres. Springs remd examd & replaced. Spring bolts remd, repd & refitted. Brake gear remd, repd & refitted. Brake shafts & brackets remd, repd & refitted. Brake Cylinder remd, repd & replaced. Cab remd repd & replaced. Clearances LF 3/8" RF 3/8" LB 3/8" RB 3/8"

Tender No 752. Axleboxes remd, repd & refitted. Brake gear remd repd & refitted. Brake shafts & brackets remd, repd & refitted. Trailing drawbar remd, repd & refitted. Buffers remd, repd & refitted. All pipes remd repd & refitted. Horn stays remd repd & refitted. Sanding gear remd, repd & refitted.

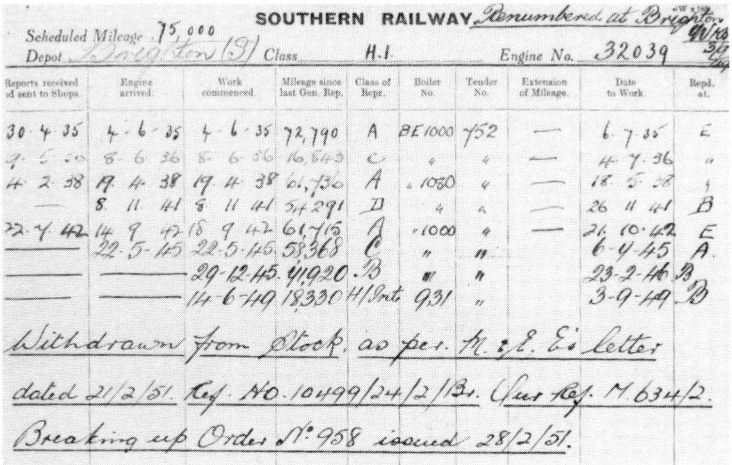

SOUTHERN RAILWAY Renumbered at Brighton

Scheduled Mileage 75,000

Depot Brighton (9) Class H.1 Engine No. 32039

Reports received and sent to Shops	Engine arrived	Work commenced	Mileage since last Gen. Rep.	Class of Repr.	Boiler No.	Tender No.	Extension of Mileage	Date to Work	Repd. at
30·4·35	4·6·35	4·6·35	72,790	A	BE1000	752	—	6·7·35	E
9·5·36	8·6·36	8·6·36	16,843	C	"	"	—	4·7·36	"
4·2·38	19·4·38	19·4·38	61,730	A	" 1080	"	—	18·5·38	"
—	8·11·41	8·11·41	54,291	B	"	"	—	26·11·41	B
22·7·42	14·9·42	18·9·42	61,715	A	" 1000	"	—	21·10·42	E
—	22·5·45	22·5·45	58,368	C	"	"		6·7·45	A.
—	—	29·12·45	41,920	B	"	"		23·2·46	B
—	—	14·6·49	18,330	H/Int.	931	"		3·9·49	B

Withdrawn from Stock as per M. & E. E's letter dated 21/2/51. Ref. HO.10499/24/2/Br. (Our Ref. M.634/2. Breaking up Order No. 958 issued 28/2/51.

Engine record card and last works repair schedule for *Hartland Point*. Only normal repairs are referred to with no comment as to the experimental modifications.

'LEADER' IN DESIGN AND CONSTRUCTION

In describing the design and construction details of the engine it is very tempting to slip into a full engineering résumè of the machine which would be singularly out of place here. Instead it is convenient to divide the locomotive into its two distinct assemblies, the main body unit and the two identical power bogies. This approach then has been taken firstly describing the various major features followed by an illustrative section.

The main body unit consisted of a full length 'fish-belly' frame which supported the boiler and ancillaries together with the fuel bunker and water tanks. All were enclosed within a framed sheet steel casing to form a central fireman's cab, with a driving cab at either end. All three cabs were interconnected by a narrow corridor on the left hand side – assuming No. 1 end (smokebox) to be to the front. To achieve this within the loading gauge and with a boiler diameter of 6ft. 4in. the boiler was offset by 6in. to the right hand side.

The two power bogies were both six-wheeled, chain coupled units. Each was driven by a three cylinder, simple expansion sleeve valve engine and fitted with Bulleid's chain driven variant of the Walschaerts valve gear. All the moving parts were flood lubricated within sheet metal oil baths, this included the spring rigging. As with *Hartland Point* the cylinders were pressure lubricated by separate means.

A study of the photographs showing the locomotive under construction reveals the extensive use of welded steel fabrication. Indeed the whole background for this was to save weight while retaining strength. The effect was to produce 'monocoque' assemblies wherever possible, leaving only those parts that may require periodic replacement as easily serviceable. All other components would only be inspected during times of major works overhaul. With the exception of the wheels, tyres, buffer stocks, axle housings and superheater, the locomotive was largely fabricated or machined from plate, sheet, tube or bar.

Such extensive use of welding was achieved by means of the electric arc which proved to be a highly successful method of marrying steel together. It was a technique unparalleled in the history of steam locomotive construction, where hitherto heavy and expensive machined castings were assembled with either bolts or rivets. Bulleid's Pacific designs had gone some way towards this goal but 'Leader' really did show the way ahead.

Of course an added bonus was that where prototype or one-off experimental work was involved any minor design changes during construction could be affected by the removal of or addition to the affected part by the welder. With the 'Leader' design incorporating so many novel features this facility was used to advantage. Components could also be easily modified where fouls or errors occurred as a side effect of other modifications.

As is referred to in the various photographs, the principles and advantages of the internal combustion engine were followed to an extent in the motion of 'Leader', although the final drive to the wheels was by chain.

Aside from the general appearance of the machine there were a number of features which were such a radical departure from tradition that they warrant a separate mention at this stage. The first concerns the final drive, which as referred to briefly above was via chain. Bulleid's object was to provide for a continuous and even torque, something not possible with a conventional coupling rod, whilst an added bonus was the almost total abolition of any hammer blow. Accordingly the centre crank axle of each bogie was provided with a sprocket on each side, to which chains led to the rear on one side and to the front on the other. Ideally a symmetrical drive on both sides would have been preferred but the constraints of the loading gauge did not allow for this. Therefore the centre and rear axles were fitted with a sprocket on one end only and were completely reversible to allow for exchange if required. Roller bearings were fitted on all axles.

Bulleid's reason for the inclusion of chains probably went back many years to the time he visited an engineering establishment in France where all the machinery was driven in this way. He had learnt at the time that chain drive required little or no maintainance and so obviously saw this as a desirable criteria to incorporate in his steam engines – hence the use of chains in the valve gear of the Pacifics. This time though the idea was taken a stage further. While there were certainly advantages with this system, the unsymmetrical drive caused obvious disadvantages, notably the unbalanced stresses acting upon the crank axle, with a pull from one side on the top and on the opposite side underneath. It was never proven, but this may well have later contributed to the crank axle failure suffered by No. 36001 on test.

The springing of the engine was also unique and besides using a conventional leaf spring, a pair of oil filled dashpots either side of the axle assisted in damping vertical movement. This was without doubt a resounding success and should have given a far better ride than any other steam engine. Unfortunately the unbalanced weight distribution tended to counter any advantages gained and a tendency to find the movement of the axleboxes within the horns rather rigid also negated its success. This in the opinion of S.C. Townroe was another factor likely to have contributed to the crank axle failure.

However, it was with the type of braking on 'Leader' that Bulleid scored an undoubted triumph. So much so that it is a wonder why such a simple principle was not utilised on other engines. As was the custom, 'Leader' was vacuum braked, but instead of a single reservoir which was manually charged by an ejector under the control of the driver, this time there were a number of separate storage tanks. Two of these were fitted at the rear end of each bogie and fed from a pair of larger storage tanks located adjacent to the smokebox. The principle was simple, on a brake application being made the bogie tanks were automatically recharged from the storage tanks, which would themselves automatically bring the ejector into use when the level of vacuum dropped to a pre-determined level. This was similar to the later concept of air-braked systems on modern diesel and electric engines; allied to which the total adhesion and clasp brakes with which the engine was fitted gave the driver confidence in control and braking power hitherto unknown with a steam design.

Left and right hand prefabricated steel box section bogie frames for one bogie and clearly showing the method of welded construction. The three triangular apertures were for access to the laminated suspension springs. The raised edges and lugs had the spring covers secured to them later. At this stage the frames were then ready to be placed in the assembly welding fixture – see next photograph. All the various bogie components then had to be welded into position including cylinders, stretchers, buffer beam etc.

National Railway Museum

A bogie frame assembly in an advanced stage of construction and shown located in the welding fixture. At this instance it is orientated in the upside down position. The frame itself could be rotated through 360 degrees to allow the welders ease of access to any section and was an idea used in Germany during World War II when 'U' boats were made in this way. As shown most of the major sub-assemblies are attached with the cylinders on the right hand side. Years later doubts would be raised as to whether the concentration of heat built up when the cylinder assembly was welded into position did not cause slight distortion to the cylinders themselves and so precipitate some of the problems encountered with the sleeve valves.

National Railway Museum

A three cylinder assembly for one of the 'Leader' bogies. Each cylinder was of 12¼in. bore by 15in. stroke and so was in itself relatively small when judged against conventional locomotive standards. This view is from the rear and shows within the bores the various inlet and outlet ports for the steam. There were 13 of each per bore, the wider ports used for the exhaust. As with the earlier experiments on No. 2039 a meehanite sleeve was later slid into each bore and when in use the whole was enveloped within a full length steam jacket. Invisible in the photograph is a separate connection for the oil pressure lubrication to the sleeves and bores. Similarly the main pipes for steam admission and exhaust to the assembly were to be added later to the top.

National Railway Museum

Sleeve valves slid into position within the cylinders. The lugs onto which the oscillating gear will later be attached can also be seen protruding from the front of each sleeve – note the angles at which the sleeves are shown as reposing were only temporary and were later altered at the time of valve setting. Within each sleeve were a number of slots machined to correspond with the slots within the cylinder casing. Through these the steam was admitted and exhausted from the pistons. Above the left hand buffer was a lifting shackle attached to an eyelet, the former is a temporary affair and would be removed before the locomotive was released for trials. Brighton works, 26.3.49.

Collection of D. Broughton

The valve gear was driven from the centre axle of each bogie and with three inside cylinders on each bogie, the centre crank axle was unusual in that it was therefore fitted with a three throw crank shaft, in some respects similar to the internal combustion engine. This view is from underneath but has been deliberately transposed to make it easier to follow. Of the features visible the three eccentric rods connecting the pistons can be seen and also the morse chain used to drive the separate valve gear crankshaft – this last named item is not visible. The large bar almost central in the view is a support for the crankshaft and the circular shaft behind the valve gear was later removed from view and sealed within the oil bath, intended to require nil maintainance, being not only flood lubricated whenever the engine was in motion but also sealed against the ingress of foreign bodies. Similar again to the principles of the internal combustion engine. Just discernable to the top right of the brake shaft is a small funnel shaped duct. This is for the disposal of smokebox ash and of course similar to the earlier experiments of 1896.

National Railway Museum

Rear view of a part completed bogie. (This is the rear bogie for No. 36001.) The two circular containers at the bottom of the view are vacuum reservoirs with a similar pair on the front bogie. Of particular interest here are the centre mounting pads for the body to sit on the bogie, two are visible along the longitudinal axis, while two more were yet to be added in a horizontal position. Each mounting consisted of a 'Mintex' pad deliberately scored with a number of grooves to act as oil channels. In this way the use of a centre pivot was avoided and was without doubt an unqualified success. The rearmost covering to the oil-bath had yet to be added, in which would be a sealed 18 in. square manhole intended for inspection purposes. A keen eye will observe the Leader-type boiler combine or manifold resting on the bench.

National Railway Museum

A wheel and crank axle set with the axlebox dampers and drive sprocket attached. The axle clearly shows two of the three cranks together with the smaller sprocket for driving the valve gear. The wheels themselves were pressed onto the axles using a 100 ton press. It was later alleged that the cranks' webs had not been supported with the customary wooden packing during this operation. The leading and trailing axles to each bogie were similar but obviously consisted of a plain unit.

National Railway Museum

Crank and plain axles depicted at Brighton after delivery from Eastleigh on 1.10.48. The external sprockets were protected against damage in transit by wooden packing. Note also the centre webs have yet to be machined.

Collection of D. Broughton

No. 1 power bogie nearing completion with the oscillating gear attached to the front of the sleeves. Again the oil bath cover to the front of this has yet to be added. Between the first and second axle is the steam turbine for driving flood lubricating oil pumps. The steps for access to the cab are probably one of the ugliest features of the whole design, yet such a style was required to allow for when the engine stopped on a curve, still permitting the driver to reach the cab with ease. The unsymmetrical drive associated with the engine is also visible and with the chain connecting centre with rear axles. On the opposite side the drive was centre to front.

National Railway Museum

As with the bogies the design of the engine from the frames upwards contained much in the way of innovation. The main frames themselves were of welded steel fabrication and braced through their length by four main stretchers and two end channels. Following the construction of a full size wooden mock up, the first pair of main frames are shown amongst an amount of clutter at Brighton Works on 11.5.48 and before the cross bracing has been added. Supporting each side were no less than 27 vertical gussets.

Collection of D. Broughton

The heart of the engine, the boiler and firebox, in the course of construction. All five 'Leader' boilers were built at Eastleigh before being moved to Brighton for incorporation into the engines. This rear view shows the barrel and crown completed with the thermic syphons supporting the crown and running down onto the continuation of the throat plate. The first section of plain sheet for the firebox (dry-side/back) is also in position at the rear. Above on the crown the two water gauges are visible. This view gives a very good impression of the advantage to be gained by the use of the syphons together with their large surface area for heat conduction. Note also that instead of stays in the syphons their place is taken by small cross tubes on the flat areas only. These provided yet further successful areas of heat transference. All this was aimed towards producing a successful steam raising vessel allied to reduced maintainance. As with other components the boiler seam was joined by welding, with the actual joints submitted to X-ray examination as a check for accuracy.

National Railway Museum

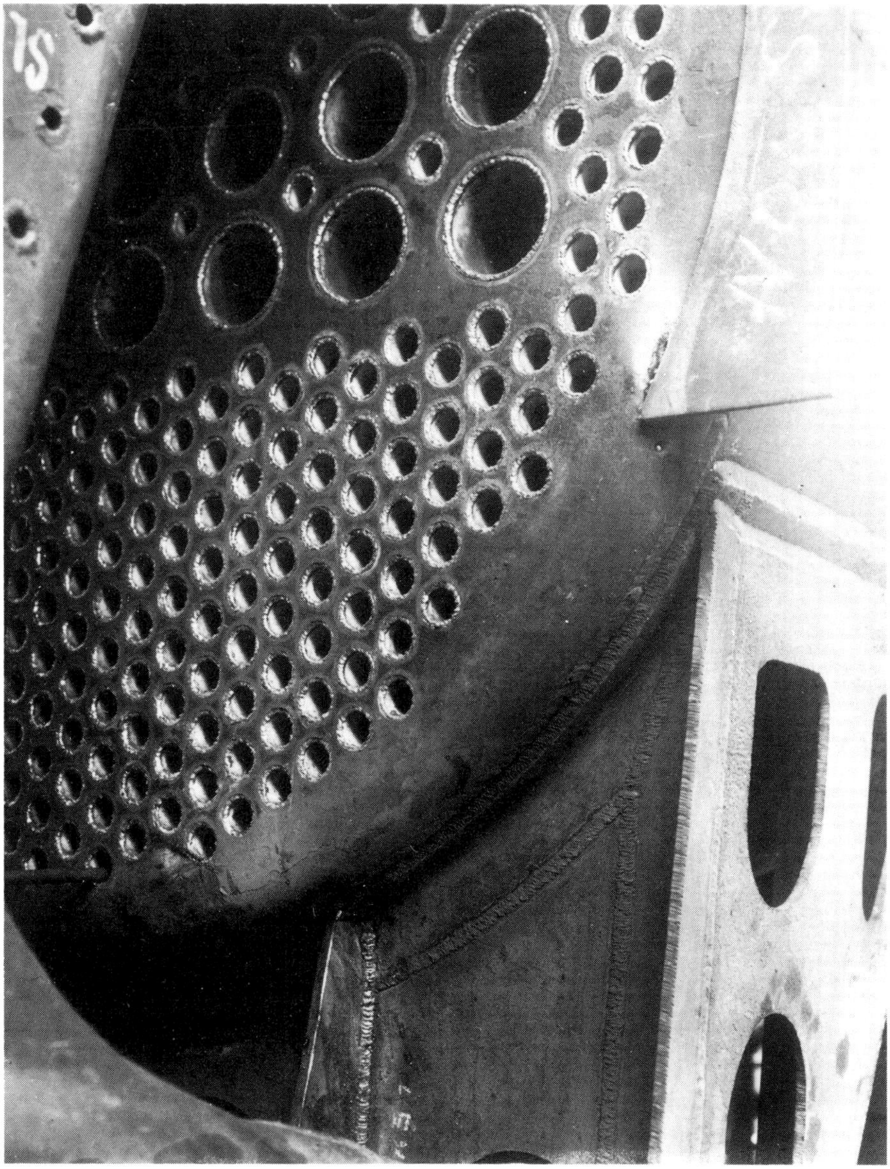

A close up of the throatplate with the tubes welded into position. Three of the small cross tubes in place of stays within the syphons, and referred to in the previous view also, show up well. Tubes were normally placed in position and the ends then expanded using special tools to provide a tight fit. The task of the boilermaker at the steam shed was to deal with any tubes which had worked loose perhaps by vibration and were thus leaking. Again, however, a thankless and time consuming job. As with the Pacifics, which were similarly fitted with welded ends to the tubes, 'Leader' never required such maintainance and this aspect of construction was another success. Altogether there were a total of 283 small or smoke tubes and 36 large superheater tubes giving a heating surface of 2,127 sq.ft. As an aside if a tube did split in service it had to be cut out and was then classed as scrap. These spent tubes were often sold to the staff as clothes posts – look in many of the gardens in Eastleigh even today!

National Railway Museum

The syphons joined to the base of the boiler just ahead of the throatplate and each was provided with a washout plug. Ahead of this the small flange was for the blowdown valve which removed sediment from the boiler water following attention from the the standard T.I.A. water treatment.
Collection of H.A.P. Browne

A 'Leader' boiler on its flat truck after transfer from Eastleigh to Brighton on 6.9.48. The dry sides to the firebox had been added, with the offset firehole door showing up well. The ribbing to the sides of the firebox was intended as additional strength against buckling and in anticipation of the considerable heat that would be generated within. The firebox itself, as first provided allowed for a grate area of 43 sq.ft., with the boiler pressure to Bulleid's standard 280 p.s.i. As with the boiler and smokebox, the firebox sides were lagged externally not only to retain heat but in an effort to reduce the temperature within the firing compartment. During assembly of the boiler within the main body unit a 'mantle shelf' tank 2in. deep was provided around the firebox, which contained water, again with the idea of heat dissipation. Unfortunately in practice the water in this small tank became so hot it raised the temperature of the main water tank and sometimes caused difficulties in getting the injectors to work.

Collection of D. Broughton

Side view of a completed boiler (again at Eastleigh) and incorporating the type of steam manifold visible on the workbench in an earlier view. At this stage the boiler is awaiting testing and has therefore had its various fittings temporarily blanked off. The leading flange for example will later form the connection to the multi-valve poppet-type regulator. Two ross-poppet type safety valves are fitted. Testing the boilers was to 350 p.s.i. under hydraulic means followed by a 290 p.s.i. steam test, both of these conducted outside the main works. An interesting point worth mentioning is that many of the views of the engine at this stage show it in photographers grey, the various parts painted in this hue so as to show up better for the official (and other!) photographers.

'R.A.' Collection

Firebricks for 'Leader' which were used to line the dry sides within the firebox. Each brick had a number cast into it to indicate its position. The various pieces connected as in a jig-saw and were secured by small hooks at the top of each row.
National Railway Museum

Rocking grate below the firebox. This was not physically attached to the boiler assembly and instead the firebox rested on the heat resistant pads to front and rear.
National Railway Museum

The hopper ashpan with the damper doors also just visible – one on either side. Note with this item construction was by a mixture of bolts and welds. The ashpan assembly hung beneath the centre of the engine and was able to discharge without difficulty into a pit without the need for manhandling back through the firehole doors.

National Railway Museum

An unusual view from beneath the main frames which shows the complexity of pipework for the injectors. The actual control spindles connected via a universal joint and ran up towards the fireman's compartment from the centre of the view. At this stage the frames and boiler were supported on a specially built wooden cradle.

National Railway Museum

Brighton Works, 26.3.49 with the boiler mounted on the frame. A careful study of the view will reveal the boiler and smokebox offset to the left of the frames to allow for the side corridor. Ahead of the boiler is the smokebox and as this will be hidden by the outer casing its design is purely functional with little in the way of aesthetic considerations. An amount of fibreglass lagging has also been applied. To the right hand side the oblong casing forms the shelf tank, which was located on the extreme side of the corridor. Although it is not referred to as such in official reports this may well have been included in an effort to reduce the uneven weight distribution caused by the offset boiler.

Collection of D. Broughton

The bunker in the course of assembly with the side panel still to be fitted. The coal space is clearly marked by the triangular section, whilst the baffles were intended not only to support the structure but to reduce water surge and are also visible. To the left is the shovel plate and unusually is positioned so that the coal had to be shovelled at 90 degrees to the bunker itself. This is within the centre or firing position of the engine. No. 2 or bunker end driving position would be at the extreme right hand side. This view was taken a few moments prior to an official photograph of the same area, the official photographer visible to the right while his assistant readies himself with a flash light. Coal capacity was 4 imperial tons, and 4000 gallons of water were also carried inclusive of the mantle and shelf tanks.

Collection of D. Broughton

Driving cab at No. 1 (smokebox) end showing the well laid out arrangement of controls and instrumentation.

National Railway Museum

A Pendant type regulator handle
B Main brake valve
C Steam reverser control
D Cylinder cock control
E Whistle valve lever (Dotted lines indicate the normal position of the hanging lever – removed at the time the view was taken.)
F Steam heating valve
G Vacuum release valve
H Windscreen wiper motor switch

Instruments

I Reverser positional indicator 'needle'
J Graduated positional quadrant plate for (I)
K Boiler steam pressure gauge
L Steam chest pressure gauge
M Duplex vacuum brake gauge
N Steam heating gauge

Electrical

O Bank of six toggle switches for route indicator lamps
P Bank of four toggle switches for cab, drawhook and instrument illumination lamps
Q Reverser control quadrant illumination
R Main instrument illumination
S Boiler pressure illumination
T Cab illumination lamp (Not shown but located above the top left hand frame of the centre window)

Components

U Corridor viewing mirror
V Drivers padded swivel seat
W Centre window catch
X Lower rollers for roller-sliding door
Y Left hand drivers door
Z Windscreen wiper motor (Blade is hidden behind regulator handle)

Adjacent to the centre window catch the whistle valve chain is hanging. A whistle isolating wheel valve was located above the right hand frame of the centre window.

Almost complete and the top body assembly is lowered onto its power bogies. Reversing was via a steam cylinder mounted underneath the body and on one side. Then via a series of shafts and couplings the reversing and cut off adjustments were transmitted equally to each bogie. Contrary to general belief the body sides were not flat but described a 50ft. inward facing curve. At this stage a degree of minor work remained, including covers to the springs, drive chains and oscillating gear and connection of the various steam pipes.

National Railway Museum

15.6.49, just one week to go and this time the painters are at work giving the engine its undercoat of black.

Collection of D. Broughton

Until now the general belief has been that 'Leader' always ran in an overall grey livery and yet here are two views taken on 20 & 21.6.49, never previously seen which should demolish such tradition. Evidently the overall black was only carried within the works and when the engine ventured out on the first trials this had been replaced by grey. In the opinion of the present writer this was a pity as lined out she would have been very smart. Certainly at that time, Brighton Works were expected to produce the latest batch of West Country engines, also in black, but in the event green was used for those engines. Drawgear was attached to the bogies themselves and a single whistle located above the windows at either end. These were independently operated.

Both collection of D. Broughton

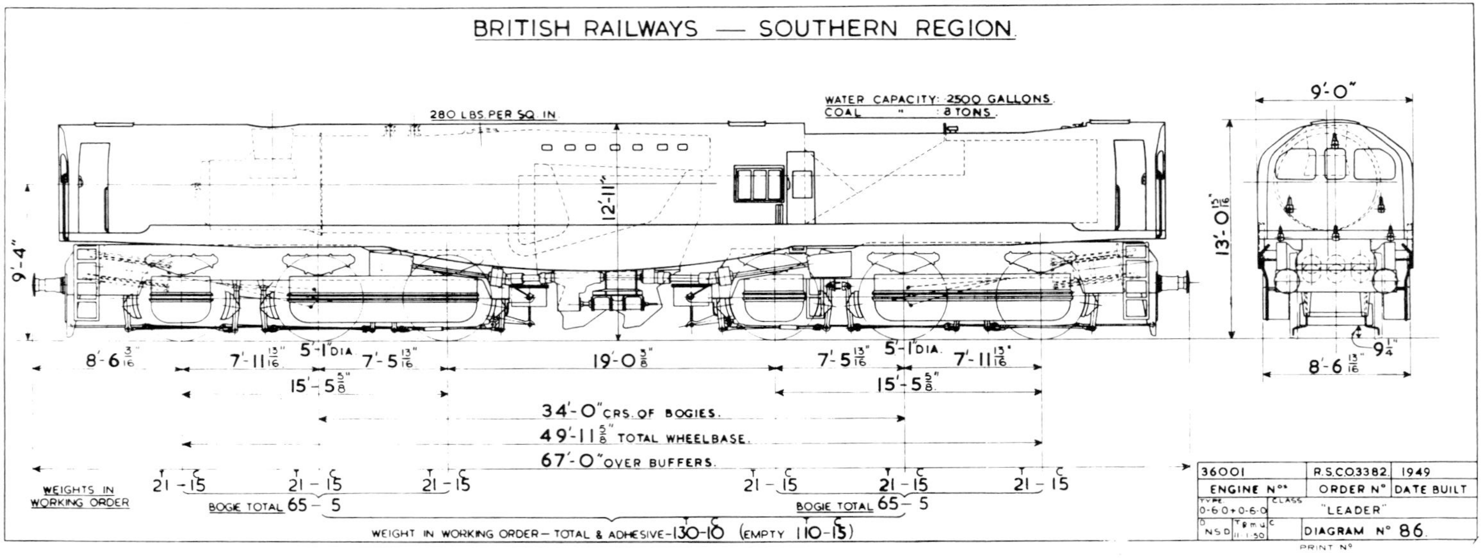

Side elevation of complete engine

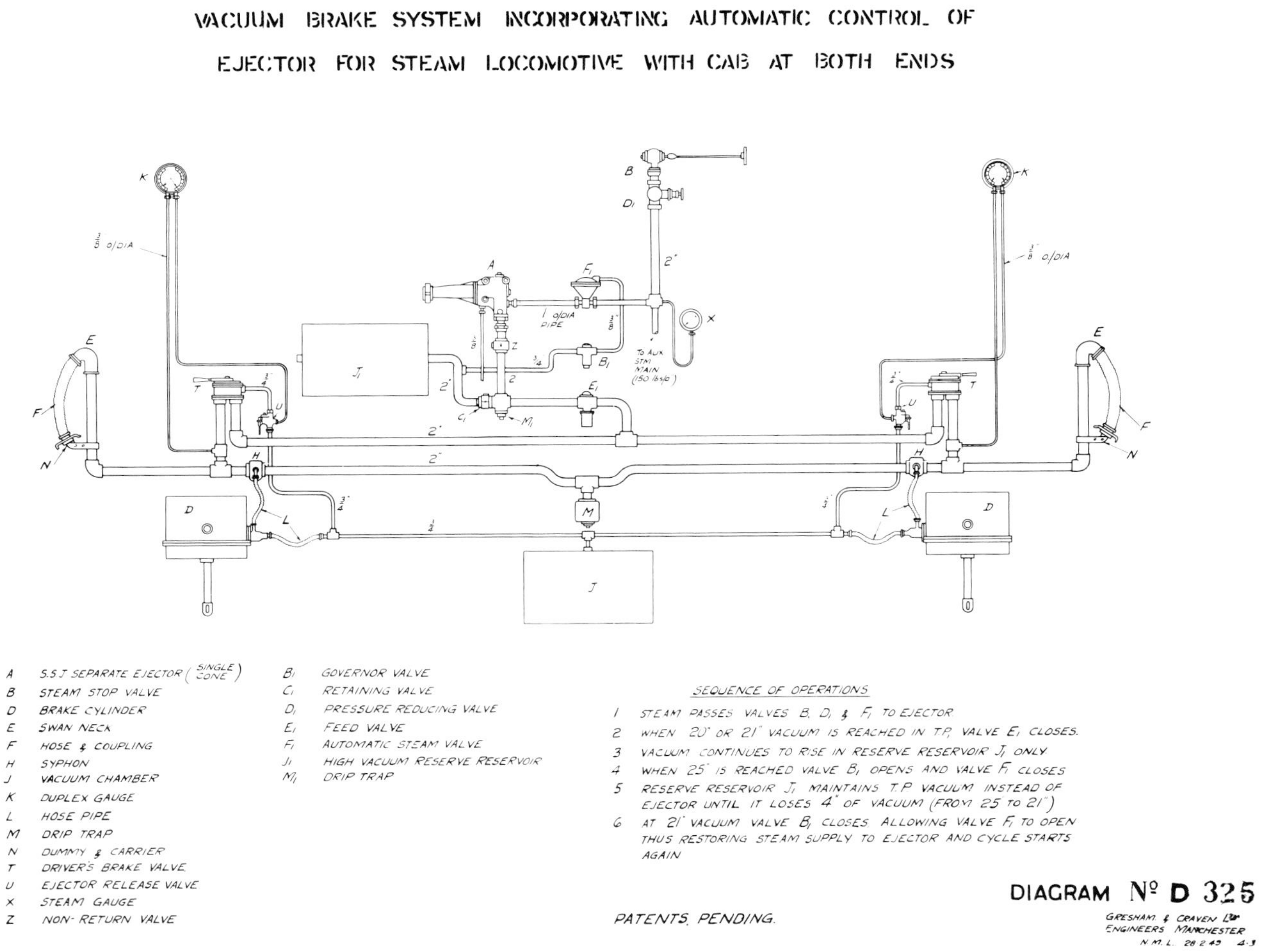

Schematic diagram of braking system

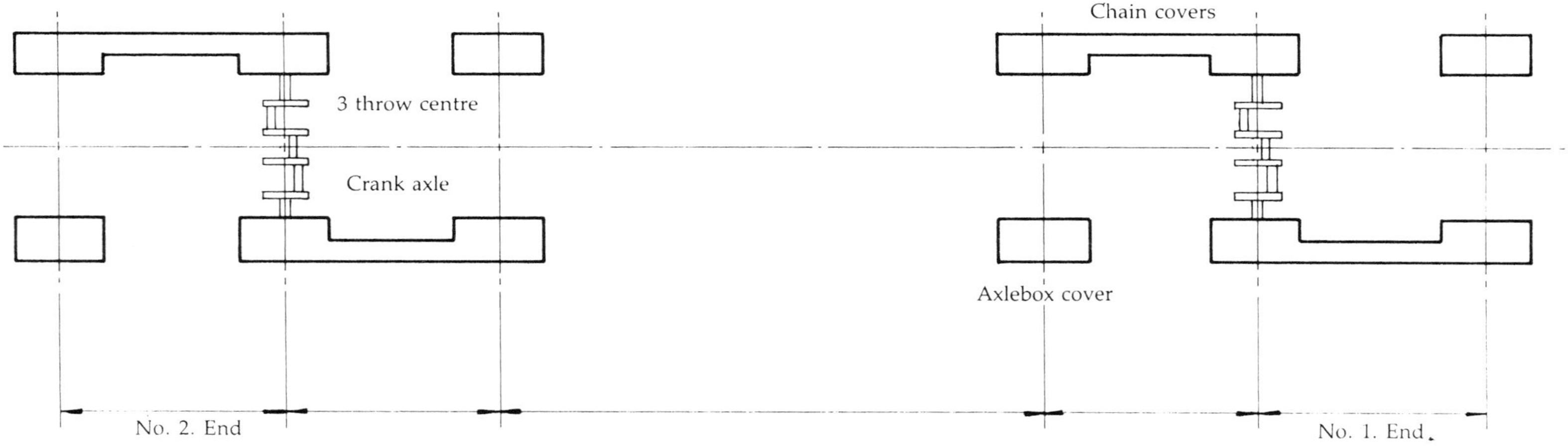

Drawing of unsymmetrical drive

'LEADER' ON TEST

Part One – The runs from Brighton

Following the satisfactory completion of the requisite stationary tests within Brighton Works, the first 'Leader' was finally ready for trials on 21 June 1949. On that morning it was hauled out into the public gaze alongside the main line by the Brighton Works shunter.

It was planned to stage the first running trial on the following day, but fate was to show its hand even at this early stage, for after running light the short distance from the works to the station, the engine failed to reverse and had to be towed back into the works for attention. Upon examination it was found that the valve operating rod to the middle sleeve on No.1 bogie was broken whilst the oscillating gear lever of the same cylinder was bent. Besides the necessary repairs the relevant parts on both bogies were strengthened.

Therefore it was not until 25 June that the delayed first trip was made. A run to Oxted via Groombridge and Lewes. As before with No. 2039 the operating authorities were taking no chances with 'Leader' and so the run was in tandem to a small tank engine. Mechanically there were no problems, even the 1 in 60 climb out of Lewes was accomplished with ease. But at Groombridge an obscure difficulty loomed, for on stopping to take on water it was found that the water column was too low to reach the high filling point on 'Leader'; so recourse had to be made to a small hose connected to a tap in the porters office! Evidently in the haste surrounding the design no one had given a thought to the fact that the water columns on the central division of the Southern were intended for engines with low filling points and so through no fault of the engine the test was abandoned and a return made to Brighton.

The following day, 26.6.49, a more successful run was made, this time along the coast line from Brighton through Chichester to Fareham and Eastleigh, in company with 'K' class mogul No. 32343.

This particular trip may well have been partly a publicity exercise aimed at the hierarchy of the Railway Executive, for No. 36001 was to remain at Eastleigh for three days during which time she was visited by a number of senior officials. In addition the engine number was painted midway along both sides and the standard 'cycling lion' BR emblem applied. Overall though the livery was still grey. In this state the locomotive was recorded by the official photographer. No attempt was made to weigh the engine and instead she was steamed for a return to Brighton, this time alone, on 29.6.49. Unfortunately the trip was not as successful as the outward run, for en route a considerable amount of knocking was heard from No. 1 bogie allied to which the exhaust was distinctly 'off-beat'.

At Brighton Works the same middle valve rod as before was found fractured, with a similar defect on the adjacent left hand rod. Examination of the associated sleeve valves also found these damaged, the centre one broken in four places and that on the left showing signs of seizure.

Brighton Station, 21.6.49. 'Leader' just emerged from the works and impatiently blows off excess steam in anticipation of its first trial run.

Collection of D. Broughton

22.6.49 and the first failure after 'Leader' refused to reverse at Brighton Station. This is the reversing gear of the engine, actuated by a small steam cylinder and intended to impart the same 'cut-off' to both bogies simultaneously.

Collection of D. Broughton

For the delayed initial trip an 'E4' tank was coupled to 'Leader' for the first run to Falmer and Groombridge. The pair are seen outside Brighton works prior to the trip. Sharp eyed readers will note no cast numberplate had as yet been fitted to No. 36001.

Collection of D. Broughton

After the embarassing experience of the first run, a crude but effective means was devised for ensuring that adequate supplies of water could be taken. This consisted of a copper chute attached to a leather bag which effectively extended the reach of the low water columns on the central division. (On the later tests from Eastleigh no such problems were encountered.) A slight disadvantage was that water tended to spray in all directions when the extension was in use! The assembly was carried on the engine for the duration of the time it was based at Brighton and here is seen in use during a pause in testing at Oxted. A useful comparison can be drawn with the height of the locomotive tender on the opposite platform.

H.W. Attwell

Bulleid felt the cause may well have been due to insufficient allowance for expansion of the sleeves within the cylinders and so all three sleeves were reduced in diameter by 0.0018in. but only on No.1 bogie.

The repairs meant the engine was out of service until 7.7.49 when light engine tests resumed. Two runs were made to Falmer and Groombridge and with a repeat working the following day. On 11 July the engine would seem to have been scheduled for a test but this was cancelled at the last moment and instead the same runs as before were made the following day, 12 July.

Two days later on the morning of 14 July, a further run was made, again light engine to Crowborough. Both Bulleid and Granshaw, the Brighton Works Manager were on the engine, which performed the task set without difficulty. During the afternoon a repeat was again attempted but this time without the designer present. At Barcombe Mills however, north of Lewes the engine failed, with all three valve rods from No. 1 bogie fractured, which also caused damage to various ancillary components. The result was a tow back to Brighton, with only 360 miles 'on the clock' from new.

Not surprisingly there was now a nine day interlude when in addition to the required repairs a number of modifications to the valve gear were undertaken. Externally too there were changes, with the grey sides lined out as panels painted in red and black.

With repairs effected 'Leader' was steamed again on 23 July running light to Crowborough without incident. The following day the destination was Seaford and again light engine. Two runs were planned to each location. But approaching Seaford on the second trip the valve gear on No. 1 bogie again developed trouble and a slow return was therefore made to Brighton. It transpired that at the time of the breakdown the

'Leader's' first visit to Eastleigh and being shunted into the Works by a grimy 'D15' No. 464. No. 36001 is shown on its blind side and is as yet un-numbered. No. 1, smokebox end is to the right. Just past the mid-way point along the casing roof are a number of small openings intended as vents to the firemans compartment. A number of others existed on the opposite side. A sliding vent in the centre of the cab roof was also located in each cab. Besides the engine the superb pole route is worthy of a second glance.

W. Gilburt

Official view of No. 1 end taken outside Eastleigh Works. Between the body unit and bogies the curved cover is the end of the oil bath behind which is the reciprocating mechanism for the sleeve valves.
National Railway Museum

engine was running in full forward gear (about 75% cut off) and at a rather higher speed than usual – this was the equivalent of running a motor car hard in first gear. But even so there must have been many puzzled faces in the works, had not the engine just run 100 miles without defect? Yet now it was the right hand valve rod that was broken along with the associated sleeve.

Why were there these continuous failures and why always the same components on the same bogie? Hindsight may provide a possible solution. Evidently whilst the engine was under construction in the works the completed No. 1 bogie was supported on blocks and supplied with steam for a static test. It ran perfectly sweetly on only an 8 p.s.i. supply, but then on instructions from a senior officer the complete assembly was put into reverse while still running forward causing considerable damage to a number of components. Most were just straightened out as best as possible afterwards.

Following repairs, which included relining both sides and part of the back of the firebox, the engine was again steamed on 12.8.49. (The reference to repairs to the firebox is interesting as at this stage no defects concerning this item are recorded in official minutes.) This was the start of a six day series of light engine tests to Crowborough – seven trips, Seaford and Lewes. The runs were marred by one failure, at Seaford on 15 August, when a pin fell out of the valve gear, but rapid repairs were made to enable the trials to continue. Even allowing for this incident the series were the most successful so far, the engine proving to be both free steaming and free running and with speeds up to 70 mph attained with ease. A note in official records against the runs relates, '. . . difficulties with the firebox lining which has a tendency to fall out of position . . . .' and '. . . control of the regulator and reverser erratic.' Perhaps a similar situation as with the previous reference to firebox repairs.

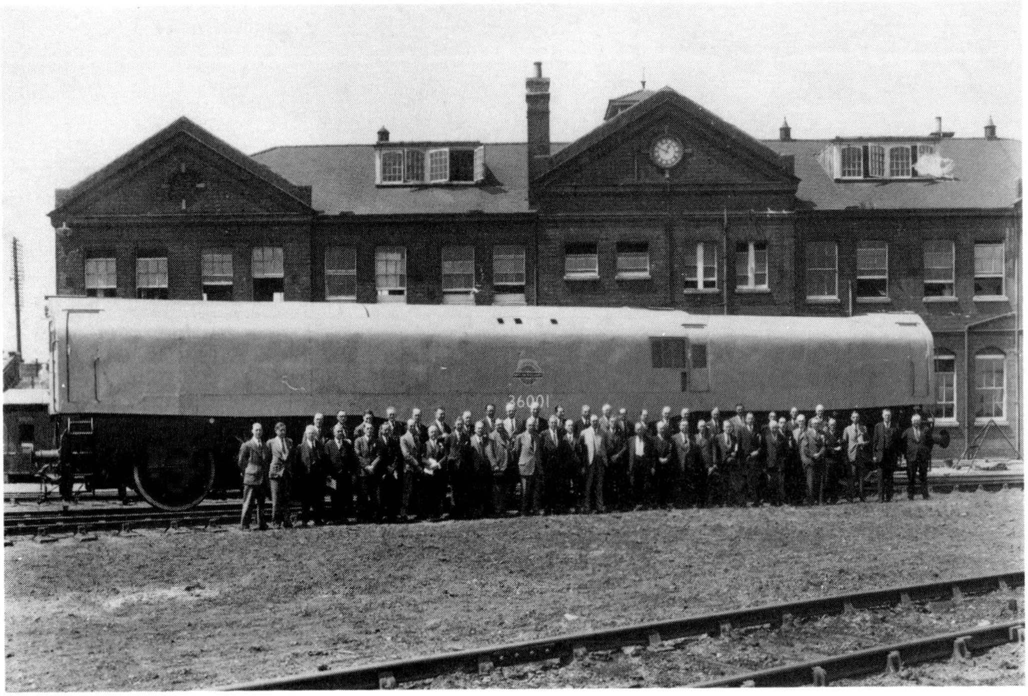

Eastleigh 28.6.49 and an inspection of 'Leader' by members of the Railway Executive and Association of Locomotive Engineers. The engine was in steam and moved up and down the yard for demonstration. Beneath the roof ventilators the 'cycling lion' BR emblem and engine number have now been applied. This together with a further coat of 'works grey' was applied in the open air of the works yard.

Collection of J. Bell

The problems with the regulator were in maintaining the desired pressure within the steam chest, also the reverser was difficult to 'notch up' (change gear).

It was inevitable that following what had been a modicum of success a load haulage trial would next be attempted. So on 18.8.49 a train of ten bogie vehicles, totalling some 248 tons was assembled in Brighton yard, which No. 36001 was set to haul to Eastleigh.

Bulleid was at this time absent from the scene, on holiday with fellow members of the Association of Railway Locomotive Engineers in Perthshire. That is not to say he was out of touch, for a series of progress telegrams were sent to his holiday hotel by Granshaw.

The actual run to Eastleigh referred to above is particuarly interesting, as conflicting reports exist as to its success. Granshaw in a telegram to Bulleid reported all was well; yet according to official records a portion of the firebox lining collapsed en route which necessitated repairs upon arrival at Eastleigh. The open ash duct in the smokebox was also welded shut at the same time after which all smokebox cleaning had to be undertaken by manual means.

At Eastleigh the opportunity was taken to weigh the engine on the works weigh table with fearful results! Instead of the 110 tons in working order of its design and as estimated from calculations during construction, the true weight turned out to be 130½ tons. The comments which must have been made by the hierarchy are not recorded – perhaps it is just as well!

No. 36001 was worked back light to Brighton on 20 August, but failed once more, this time at Barnham. Again the cause was due to breakage of the sleeve valve on No. 1 bogie, the firebox lining also refused to stay in place.

Stationary at Lewes on 17.8.49 with a fair gathering of interested onlookers. The not inconsiderable amount of black smoke would indicate the fire was built up whilst the engine was standing. Any enquiry as to the machine by a member of the public was greeted with the response that all was well.

Collection of H.C. Casserley

Receiving attention inside Brighton Works in August 1949 and with the oil bath cover of the oscillating gear removed on No. 1 bogie. A minor point is that the engine now had its lining out applied on top of the grey livery while the painted number has been removed from the centre of the sides to near the cab doors.

Collection of D. Broughton

Another failure, this time at Barnham on 20.8.49 when returning to Brighton from Eastleigh. On this occasion there was a broken sleeve on No. 1 bogie along with difficulties with the firebox lining.

W.N.J. Jackson

Back at Brighton another nine days were spent out of service enabling repairs and modificatons to take place. These included reducing the maximum cut-off from 75–65%, a spark arrester was supposedly fitted at this point.

Trials recommenced on 30.8.49 the engine running light to Crowborough. These continued until 2 September and were marred only once by a single firebrick coming loose. (Accordingly, with confidence again restored, on 5.9.49 the most ambitious test to date was set.) No. 36001 was to haul eight bogie vehicles totalling 260 tons to Victoria via Oxted. This was of course only slightly heavier than that previously taken to Eastleigh but unfortunately the run was terminated at Oxted as there were difficulties in maintaining the required steam pressure, despite a stop for a 'blow-up' at Dormans. The return from Oxted was light engine.

Brighton were of the opinion that the spark arrester may have been partly to blame for the difficulties encountered so it was removed, the same trial was then rearranged for 8.9.49. However, fate was to determine that London would never witness a 'Leader' in steam, for once again the test was terminated at Oxted for exactly the same reasons as before. This it should be said was not due to any fault on the part of the driver and fireman who had both manfully struggled with their tasks in an attempt to retain sufficient boiler pressure. Once more then it returned light to Brighton.

A successful trip to London would no doubt have been an ego-boosting exercise for the design, although, against the available evidence the decision to curtail the trial was the only one possible. It was one thing to disrupt the sporadic service on the relatively

Running light near Lewes following repairs. To provide slightly easier access to the front of the valves the flexible pipe for the steam heating to a following train had been removed although it was later replaced. For the same reason the oil bath cover is missing and while this allowed the operation of the motion to be observed with the engine running – after removal of sections of the floor – a side effect was that dirt and grit could also enter. The very items the cover and oil bath were intended to keep out. We shall never know if such ingress of foreign bodies precipitated any of the valve failures.

C.C.B. Herbert

Dormans, September 1949 and time for a 'blow-up' on the return to Brighton from Oxted after an abortive attempt to reach Victoria. 'Leader' had failed to surmount the 1 in 210 climb to the station with a trailing load of 260 tons. Included with the group on the platform is W.H. 'Joe' Hutchinson who had so much to do with the engine from its inception on the drawing board.

H.W. Attwell

The end of the platform at Brighton afforded a good view of the running shed. 'Leader' framed between 'Q1' No. 33040 and diesel shunter DS1173 and perhaps awaiting a test run.
Collection of D. Broughton

quiet route through Oxted, but the resulting hold-ups caused by a failure nearer London would have been chaotic.

Investigation now centred on two problems, poor steaming and the instability of the firebox lining. Regarding the former, it was felt that the fault lay with the front end design and so the size of the chokes were altered within the multiple jet blast pipe. At the same time a new and, it was hoped, more resilient type of firebrick lining was fitted.

Trials recommenced on 16.9.49, with No. 36001 twice taking empty coaching stock to Crowborough and return. There were no problems with either the firebox or valve gear this time but still the steaming difficulties persisted. After a further modification to the blast pipe a repeat run was made three days later but once more with the same difficulties.

Following yet another modification to the blast pipe the engine was again set to haul an empty stock train to Crowborough. However, at Uckfield it was the turn of the valve gear to play up again, with a fracture of the middle sleeve on No. 1 bogie at the point where the extending 'ears' were attached to the oscillating gear. With the appropriate gear dismantled by the fitter who accompanied the engine on every trial an ignominious return was made to Brighton.

Two days, 21/22 September were spent in the works under repair, during which time besides making good the obvious repairs, two very interesting modifications were carried out. The first involved the removal of the sleeve oscillating gear from No. 1 bogie and steel valve guides replaced the mechanite liners. How much of this can be credited to Bulleid is uncertain for as time went on more and more control was being exercised from the Railway Executive. Bulleid even had to get permission from this organisation to travel on his own engine! Another repair was to the lower firebricks, some of which were found to be badly worn and reported 'patched' as needed.

In disgrace at Uckfield on 20.9.49. As well as the crew a fitter was present throughout the trials, whilst it was also common for a number of other observers to be carried. The engine had failed with a broken sleeve valve.

H.W. Attwell

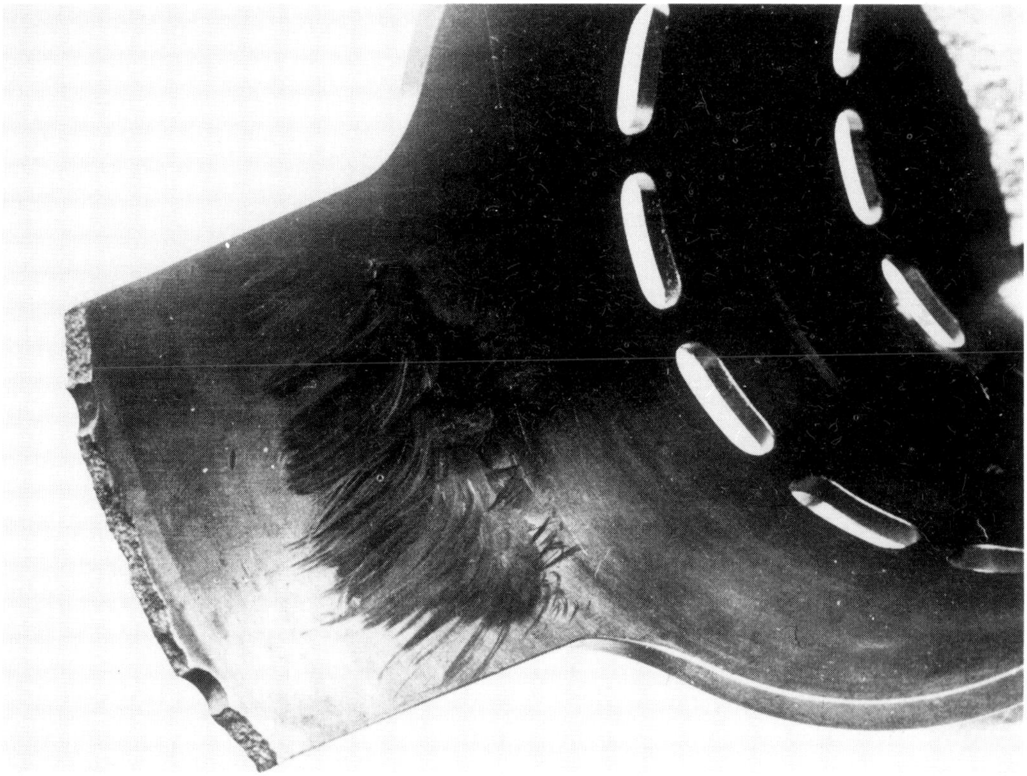

A failed sleeve valve on 'Leader', possibly as a result of the incident at Uckfield, although to be fair there were several such occurances. The broken casting should have continued on to form the lugs to which the oscillating gear was attached. The score marks both within the sleeve and at the end are likely to have been caused by the sticking of the valve during its movement. After a number of similar failures the oscillating gear was eventually removed from both bogies.

National Railway Museum

The changes were tested by running light to Crowborough from 23 to 25 September. A total of five round trips amounting to some 235 miles. Other than slight attention to the firebricks after the last journey no problems were encountered. Accordingly further runs with load haulage were commenced, these started on 27.9.49 and involved 5 bogie vehicles weighing 150 tons to either Crowborough, Lewes or Oxted. The runs continued until the last day of the month by which time 447 miles had been covered with no mechanical difficulties reported, although steaming was once again erratic.

A repeat series was arranged, commencing on 3.10.49, but in addition to the poor steaming the firebox brickwork was found to be in poor condition after the last run. Also a new problem had emerged, for on the first day both chains on the oil circulating pump came off, and on the second day of the trials the governer valve of the same pump was suspect. Both these were potentially serious failures, for without a guarantee of adequate lubrication the likelihood of seizure increased.

Repairs were again undertaken at Brighton, the firebricks being replaced by a cast iron type, possibly the first time such items had been used in a railway environment.

Tests resumed on 9.10.49 with No. 36001 set to take 150 tons to Groombridge. At Crowborough, however, the trial was halted, the cast iron firebricks having melted into the fire on one side and were threatening to do the same on the opposite side. This caused the metal side sheet of the firebox to become red hot, making it impossible to continue if only for the sake of the firemen. Ironically, despite all this radiant heat percolating around the interior of the engine there had still been problems with poor steaming! After allowing matters to cool off sufficiently the return to Brighton was minus a train.

This last failure is of special interest because of the questions it raised. Firstly, the use of cast iron firebricks is in itself open to question, especially as the heat needed to raise the temperature enough to melt cast iron indicated a terrific draw on the fire. The fault

Driver Bill Long (left), Fireman Ted Forder (centre) and a Brighton fitter at Crowborough 9.10.49 the occasion of the melted fire bricks. All three were no doubt glad to escape from the torrid interior of the engine on that occasion. Apart from the fitter carried on every trip, there was one run when no less than 18 others were on board the engine, no doubt causing conditions to become a bit cramped. The fitters were not provided with any special tools and so the amount of repairs undertaken en route was restricted. The three men, together with Mr Attwell, who was also on board, were waiting for the firebox sides to cool down before returning to Brighton. Unfortunately this was not the first failure of the refractory bricks and on every occasion this occurred the dry sides of the firebox would distort a little more with the heat and meant the replacement bricks were even more likely to fall down.

H.W. Attwell

Brighton shed and the engine being made ready for a day's testing. Bill Long is in the driver's cab and Ted Forder leaning from the fireman's window. Ted was the fireman on all the runs from Brighton and in conversation with Les Warnett is reported as holding very different views on the engine compared with many. He recounts the troubles with overheating in the centre compartment were greatly exaggerated, the engine cooler than a 'West Country' on a summers day and far preferable. Stories of him having to visit his G.P. after firing the engine are totally unfounded. Likewise he had no objections to working No. 36001 with No. 1 end leading and indeed this was often necessary due to the destinations chosen. The acceleration and braking were described as 'excellent' and certainly equal to the electric units he has driven since. Raising steam too was simple, the ability of the boiler to generate steam in a short space of time was better than a Brighton 'Terrier'.

W.N.J. Jackson

was clearly apparent even then, the steam that was being produced was not being used to best effect. Yet it would appear little attempt was made to rectify what was beginning to show up as a serious design defect. However, before apportioning blame it may well have been that any attempt at a redesign would have possibly brought permanent condemnation from the Railway Executive, so it became a question of attempting to prove the locomotive as sufficiently viable as it stood. Perhaps they felt the chance for rebuilding where necessary would come later. These conclusions are born out following Riddles memorandum of March 1950 (See Appendix G).

The firebox was now relined with conventional material. A new design of brick some 3½in. thick being used. Larger holding hooks were also added.

More tests began on 22.10.49, continuing until the 24th. As before 150 tons was taken to the same destinations. The first two days were successful enough but on the last day the middle sleeve from No. 2 bogie broke while running near Lewes. Examination showed the failure was probably due to fatigue affecting the sleeve 'ears' and so the same modifications that had earlier been undertaken on No. 1 bogie were made, this included the removal of the oscillating gear.

Road runs recommenced on 29.10.49 and at last it looked as if success was within

The creations of Bulleid and Riddles side by side outside Brighton. With the removal of the oil bath cover and gear from the front bogie 'Leader' presents a decidedly naked appearance.
Collection of D. Broughton

reach; for between this date and 16.12.49 no less than 27 days were utilised for test runs, all but three attached to a trailing load. There was even a nine day period in November (although not consecutive days), when an aggregate of 100 miles daily was successfully undertaken and on each occasion again with a trailing load.

The loads hauled varied and included either a five or eight coach empty train of between 153 and 255 tons. A number of defects were reported including broken valve rods and circlips. (Full details of the tests are given in the chronology at the end of this chapter.)

As with previous runs with No. 2039, most of the tests involving No. 36001 commenced from Brighton station. The traffic department providing whatever vehicles they had available to the approximate tonnage stipulated. This accounts for the variance experienced in the daily loadings.

But even if the prototype was perhaps beginning to justify its design, back at Brighton works there was considerable gloom. For BR Headquarters were closely in touch with the progress of the trials and consequently aware of the numerous failures that had occurred earlier. Accordingly a directive was issued on 19.11.49 that work was to cease on the other 'Leader' engines then under construction. This was especially unfortunate for No. 36002 as she was only two days away from completion. Indeed had it not been for the amount of works time her elder sister had spent receiving attention No. 36002 would already have been under test.

It was intended to commence a further series of runs on 14.12.49 but the operating department advised the works that they were unable to supply either the stock or men owing to the build up of the peak holiday season. 'Leader's' last run of the year was on

Running between Brighton and Lewes during November 1949, the headcode was one applicable to trains destined for the Oxted line. This was perhaps the 'best side' of the engine, the windows and door to the fireman's compartment breaking up the plainness of the opposite side. A set of steps afforded access to this centre compartment after which there was a step down into a slight well which formed the floor.

Times Newspapers Ltd

On test 22.11.49, the engine was by now decidedly grubby in appearance. The modifications that had been carried out to the blastpipe were by this time sufficient to promote reasonable steaming and reduce the amount of fire throwing from the chimney. Unfortunately a side effect was a tendency for the fire to creep backwards and lick around the firehole door.

British Railways

No. 1 end leading near Lewes, with the elbow and arm of an unknown individual protruding from the firemans compartment. Temperatures of 122° F were recorded at the window of the centre compartment which allied to the ever present condensation helped give the engine its nickname, 'The Chinese Laundry'. This was not a particularly excessive reading for the engine as other parts, notably the passage alongside the boiler and No. 1 end cab were reputedly hotter – the latter because of the proximity of the smokebox door. The 122° however was considered a fair average.
Times Newspapers Ltd

16 December when she was worked light to Eastleigh again for weighing, she returned the same day. The engine then re-entered the works where it was to remain until 26.1.50. (A record of the weighings of the engine is given in Appendix D.)

So why the period of store for so long after the holiday period, especially when the tests were at last going well? Certainly this was not now due to staff or stock shortage. Instead the answer to this probably lies in the now generally known true weight of the engine. The Chief Civil Engineers department had been made aware of the figures and were understandably perturbed by its possible effect upon both track and bridges. Such concern heightened over the side to side weight variance. Brighton works thus spent time attempting to produce a more stable balance which included two complete changes of springs. A number of other modifications unconnected with the weight problem were also carried out and included work to the brakes, valve gear, lubricators and whistle. Moving ahead in time it was to transpire that the difficulties with the firebox lining had at last been overcome, although to remedy this 9in. wide firebricks were fitted to the lower course. This effectively reduced the grate area from 43 to 25.5 sq.ft., only 5 sq.ft. larger than an M7 tank.

Eight vehicles equal to approximately 250 tons being taken up the 1 in 88 of Falmer Bank near Brighton on the morning of 4.12.49, evidently with consummate ease. The hill climbing abilities of 'Leader' are remembered as considerable, although this was an aspect never fully recounted in official reports. On one particular occasion the 4¾ miles from Buxted to Crowborough were covered in 4½ min, exactly half the scheduled time. Neither was this a unique example, for the same times were repeated the following day. Unfortunately on both occasions the trailing load is not recorded. Such efforts on behalf of both engine and crew were often at the behest of the observers carried. Bulleid himself perhaps saying ' . . . come on, let us get to the top as quick as possible, then if anything is going to fail we will will find out what and why'. Ironically on such occasions failures were rare, although the unexpected demands for steam meant pressure would perhaps fall to only 120 p.s.i. Bulleid is also recalled as being particularly generous on the occasions he travelled and regularly gave the crew £1 between them after every run. Other officials too are recalled for their generosity, one man sharing bars of chocolate with the driver and fireman at a time when such luxury was difficult to obtain.

W.N.J. Jackson

Following this period in store, No. 36001 was steamed on 27.1.50 for a light engine trial to Tunbridge Wells after which further spring adjustments and weighings, this time at Brighton, took place. A few days later on 2.2.50 she ran light to Eastleigh and was again weighed.

The sphere of activity now moves away from the engine itself and instead to the Railway Executive. Robert Riddles, C.M.E. for the whole of BR was understandably concerned over the length of time already undertaken on trials together with the erratic behaviour of the engine. At his request R.G. Jarvis from Brighton prepared a detailed report on progress to date;

LEADER CLASS LOCOMOTIVE

'I have been asked by Mr. Warder (the new Mechanical & Electrical Engineer of the Southern Region) to express my views on this experiment as the Regional Chief Technical Assistant responsible for design. No personal criticism is inferred in the remarks which follow, and the views expressed represent my views which may well be at variance with those of the designers of the locomotive, on the basis that if doctors can differ so may engineers.

The design has certain attractive features, it has many problems to solve, and it has some fundamental defects. That the locomotive could be made to work I have no doubt, but a great deal of experimental work will be necessary. It all depends upon how much money can be permitted for the modifications which will entail virtually a complete re-arrangement.'

The main disadvantages were then listed as follows;

1. The weight will restrict route availaility.
2. The enclosure and lubrication of engines, axleboxes and springs is very unsatisfactory.
3. The increased steam chest volume and port areas and the reduced clearance volumes, may only have a minimal effect on thermal efficiency.
4. Replacement of firebox water-legs by firebricks is not successful.

He continued;

'The disappointing progress made with the locomotive to date is to a much greater extent attributable to the detail design than to the broad conception.'

Continuing on the same theme the following changes were then listed as essential if the locomotive was to be made serviceable;

1. Self aligning bearings are essential.
2. Changes will have to be made to the fireman's compartment, this being very unsatisfactory and dangerous in the event of a blow back upon entering a tunnel.
3. Development work is required to alleviate the problems with the sleeve valve.
4. If it were possible smaller wheels would be deemed preferable.'

Shortly afterwards on 24.3.50 Riddles submitted his own report to the Railway Executive in which he summarised the findings to date as well as putting forward his own recommendations;

'. . . . it has not so far been possible to release this locomotive for revenue earning service.

In view of the special character of this locomotive and to ensure continuity in the work necessary to overcome the difficulties which were experienced, an invitation was extended to Mr. Bulleid, prior to his retirement in September 1949, to remain closely in touch with the developments necessary and supervise any alterations required to ensure that the locomotive should become successful. It was originally thought that 3 months would be sufficient for this work to be completed but in the light of later experience the arrangement with Mr. Bulleid was continued a further 3 months until the end of March this year.

Mr. Bulleid has now intimated his desire to be released from his obligations in this respect and has submitted a memorandum on the subject of the locomotive.' (See Appendix F)

Riddles then dealt with a number of other matters and costings before continuing;

> 'In view of the unsatisfactory weight distribution and reports of track spreading allegedly due to this locomotive (these were never proven – KJR), trial runs were recently discontinued. Steps are being taken which it is hoped will improve the weight distribution sufficiently to permit a resumption of trial runs, probably at restricted speeds and with a limited amount of coal and water on board. Although the radius of action of the locomotive will be limited by the restrictions on the amount of coal and water carried which it may be necessary to impose, further trial runs will enable proof of performance of the firebox lining and valve mechanism, as already modified, to be obtained. Dynamometer car tests with suitable loads will be conducted to obtain data on coal and water consumption in relation to work done. If the dynamometer car tests do in fact reveal that substantially less fuel and water are required per unit of work done compared with the normal locomotive, consideration will be given to carrying out the further modifications necessary before the locomotive can hope to fulfil its designers expectations.'

Riddles had thus made no attempt to gloss over the failings that had already occurred. Indeed there were a number of members of the Railway Exectutive who were in favour of curtailing the project even at that point. So the emphasis once more returns to Brighton and No. 36001, with everything still at stake and yet with the odds already stacked against success.

Bulleid's feelings upon hearing of this news are not recorded, ensconsed as he was in a new position as C.M.E. of the Irish Railway system. Brighton Works however had been instructed to press ahead with the trials and modifications and so began a number of changes which included the oil supply to the pedestal guides. As a result the riding qualities improved dramatically, the previous harshness now giving way to a smoothness more akin to a passenger carriage.

Leaving Brighton on another test. The high angle of the photograph just shows the opening for the coal bunker at No. 2 end. In the right background are a number of other engines including *Hartland Point*. On one occasion when the Chief Locomotive Tester was travelling alone in the rear cab, two loud cracks were heard which were immediately taken to indicate another sleeve valve failure. It transpired to be nothing more serious than the engine having run over two detonators.
Collection of D. Broughton

In store at Brighton during the winter of 1949/50, with the lower half of the oil bath covers removed from the axles at No. 1 end. Due to the weight of the engine, speed on the later trials was restricted to 50 mph, with a maximum of 3 tons of coal and 2600 gallons of water on board. By this time a number of modifications had been made to the engine, one of the more recent being the sealing off of the pressure relief valves on the cylinders. This action was somewhat drastic for all that was really required was some stronger springs.

W.N.J. Jackson

Elsewhere the Southern Region M. & E.E's department had been instructed to prepare for the dynamometer car trials. Originally these were to have been from Brighton but with the C.C.E. now aware of the true axle weight of the engine which verged on 25 tons (This was the maximum side to side axle weight and not the equal measurement.) he promptly banned any further test running on the Central Section. Bulleid was also alledged to have said at one time '. . . send it to Eastleigh, they will get it going . . .', and it was indeed Eastleigh that was chosen for the trials. No. 36001 steaming away from Brighton for the last time on 13.4.50, some no doubt glad to see it go.

CHRONOLOGY

Trial running from Brighton. 22.6.49–2.2.50.

*	22. 6.49	Initial trial trip
	25. 6.49	Light with E4 tank to Falmer and Groombridge.
	26. 6.49	Light with K class 2-6-0 to Eastleigh.
*	29. 6.49	Light engine Eastleigh to Brighton.
	7. 7.49	Light engine to Falmer and Crowborough.
	8. 7.49	Light engine to Falmer and Crowborough.
	12. 7.49	Light engine to Falmer and Crowborough.
*	14. 7.49	Light to Crowborough, twice.
	23. 7.49	Light to Crowborough.
*	24. 7.49	Light to Seaford.
*	12. 8.49	Light to Crowborough, Seaford and Lewes.
	13. 8.49	Light to Crowborough, Seaford and Lewes.
*	14. 8.49	Light to Crowborough, Seaford and Lewes.
*	15. 8.49	Light to Crowborough, Seaford and Lewes.
*	16. 8.49	Light to Crowborough, Seaford and Lewes.
*	17. 8.49	Light to Crowborough, Seaford and Lewes.
*	18. 8.49	Trial to Eastleigh with 248 tons.
*	20. 8.49	Light Eastleigh to Brighton.

	30. 8.49	Light to Crowborough.
	31. 8.49	Light to Crowborough.
	1. 9.49	Light to Crowborough.
*	2. 9.49	Light to Crowborough.
*	5. 9.49	Intended trial to Victoria with 260 tons.
*	8. 9.49	Intended trial to Victoria with 260 tons.
*	16. 9.49	Trail to Crowborough. Load between 180 and 271 tons.
*	19. 9.49	Trail to Crowborough. Load between 180 and 271 tons.
*	20. 9.49	Trail to Crowborough. Load between 180 and 271 tons.
	23. 9.49	Light to Crowborough.
	24. 9.49	Light to Crowborough.
*	25. 9.49	Light to Crowborough.
*	27. 9.49	Trials to Oxted, Crowborough and Lewes. Load 150 tons.
*	28. 9.49	Trials to Oxted, Crowborough and Lewes. Load 150 tons.
*	29. 9.49	Trials to Oxted, Crowborough and Lewes. Load 150 tons.
*	30. 9.49	Trials to Oxted, Crowborough and Lewes. Load 150 tons.
*	3.10.49	Trials to Crowborough. Load 150 tons.
*	4.10.49	Trials to Crowborough. Load 150 tons.
*	9.10.49	Trials to Crowborough. Load 150 tons.
	22.10.49	Trials to Oxted and Crowborough. Load 150 tons.
	23.10.49	Trials to Oxted and Crowborough. Load 150 tons.
*	24.10.49	Trials to Oxted and Crowborough. Load 150 tons.
*	29.10.49	Light to Crowborough and Tunbridge Wells
	30.10.49	Light to Crowborough and Tunbridge Wells
	31.10.49	Trial to Crowborough. Load 161 tons.
*	1.11.49	Trials to Oxted and Crowborough. Load 153–255 tons.
	2.11.49	Trials to Oxted and Crowborough. Load 153–255 tons.
	3.11.49	Trials to Oxted and Crowborough. Load 153–255 tons.
	4.11.49	Trials to Oxted and Crowborough. Load 153–255 tons.
	7.11.49	Trials to Oxted, Polegate and Crowborough. Load 153–255 tons.
	8.11.49	Trials to Oxted, Polegate and Crowborough. Load 153–255 tons.
	9.11.49	Trials to Oxted, Polegate and Crowborough. Load 153–255 tons.
	10.11.49	Trials to Oxted, Polegate and Crowborough. Load 153–255 tons.
	11.11.49	Trials to Oxted, Polegate and Crowborough. Load 153–255 tons.
*	16.11.49	Trial to Oxted. Load 255 tons
	21.11.49	Trials to Oxted and Polegate. Load 153–255 tons.
	22.11.49	Trials to Oxted and Polegate. Load 153–255 tons.
	23.11.49	Trials to Oxted and Polegate. Load 153–255 tons.
	24.11.49	Trials to Oxted and Polegate. Load 153–255 tons.
*	25.11.49	Trials to Oxted and Polegate. Load 153–255 tons.
*	29.11.49	Trial to Polegate. Load 153 tons.
	1.12.49	Trials to Polegate, Oxted, Tunbridge Wells and Groombridge. Load 153–255 tons.
	2.12.49	Trials to Polegate, Oxted, Tunbridge Wells and Groombridge. Load 153–255 tons.
	3.12.49	Trials to Polegate, Oxted, Tunbridge Wells and Groombridge. Load 153–255 tons.
	4.12.49	Trials to Polegate, Oxted, Tunbridge Wells and Groombridge. Load 153–255 tons.
	5.12.49	Trials to Polegate, Oxted, Tunbridge Wells and Groombridge. Load 153–255 tons.
*	6.12.49	Trials to Polegate, Oxted, Tunbridge Wells and Groombridge. Load 153–255 tons.
	12.12.49	Trials to Crowborough and Oxted. Load 153–255 tons
*	13.12.49	Trials to Crowborough and Oxted. Load 153–255 tons.
	16.12.49	Light to Eastleigh and return.
	27. 1.50	Light to Tunbridge Wells.
	2. 2.50	Light to Eastleigh and return

* Signifies runs classed as failures.

A JUSTIFICATION TO SURVIVE

Part Two – The tests from Eastleigh

'Leader' was moved from Brighton on 13.4.50 and spent four days in store at Eastleigh before entering the works under whose auspices it would now remain. Prior to the dynamometer car tests the works were to continue to try to overcome the problem of the unbalanced weight distribution and, it was decided to add balancing weights within the corridor space at floor level. These took the form of several transverse struts filled with old brake blocks, firebars and other items of pig iron to a cumulative depth of almost 2ft. Even such drastic measures were insufficient and recourse had to be made to pieces of slab steel, both underneath the floor and vertically along the inside of the casing. An extra 5¼ tons was added in this way.

At the same time additional distance pieces were tried under the spring spigots. The final result was a far more acceptably balanced engine but one which now possesed a

No. 36001 inside Eastleigh running shed and probably soon after transfer from Brighton. It is reported that at no time was a boiler washout ever carried out on the engine. The T.I.A. water treatment was sufficient to prevent the accumulation of scale. This treatment involved the use of the manual blow down cock, with the discharge via the outlet near the throatplate, this was recalled as a very noisy operation. It is also reported that tube cleaning was rarely, if ever performed.

Collection of Les Warnett

Just passing Eastleigh South en-route for Fratton. No. 36001 is at the head of what appears to be a five-coach train.

S.C. Townroe

maximum axle loading of 24½ tons, 25% greater than that originally intended. With work hampered by pressure from more mundane matters it was not until the end of May that the engine was once again ready for service.

Because of all this extra weight, fresh authority had to be obtained from the Chief Civil Engineer for the engine to run at all. A decision was made allowing trials to be be undertaken only on routes cleared for the Merchant Navy class. The 50 mph speed limit imposed during the latter part of 1949 was also confirmed as were the restrictions in the amount of coal and water that could be carried. All this was intended to reduce the risk of damage to trackwork and bridges.

By 5.6.50, final adjustments of the ballast weights were complete and the engine was deemed ready for the next series of trials. It had been notified by now that it was the Eastern Region dynamometer car that would be used for the comparative tests, this particular vehicle having recorded the highest ever speed for a steam engine when run behind the world record holder *Mallard* in 1938. This time though high speed was not what was required, instead it was a justification for the future survival of No. 36001 and her sisters. Indeed, much would depend upon the data received.

Preliminary trials commenced on 6.6.50, with 'Leader' taking a rake of 10 coaches weighing some 332 tons over the 18 or so miles from Eastleigh to Fratton and return. The engine was initially handled by the works trials crew, although a number of other observers were also on board.

Short as it was, the run was not without its amusing incident. For as one of the works fitters recalled, ' . . . . when running well near Botley there was a lurch caused by the track, immediately following which a signal post came within a whisper of being wiped out . . . . we all held our breath.' The intention of the preliminary trials was to show up any minor modifications needed before the full dress runs and early results were

At Eastleigh again and on another of the preliminary trials to Fratton. The lighter coloured panel towards the centre of the engine was where the BR emblem had once been affixed. Why this was removed is unclear, was someone embarrased perhaps by the venture even at the start?

Collection of Mrs Talbot

Awaiting departure from Fratton for what was probably Eastleigh even if the headcode refers to the coast line to Brighton. The available line capacity on the Botley and Fareham line was the reason this was chosen for the early tests.

D.R. Yarney

promising. The return working for example was brought to a standstill near Eastleigh South Signalbox and then pulled away without a trace of hesitation or slip and still with a trailing load of 332 tons.

Following two more days on which similar tests were made, 'Leader' was stopped on 9.6.50 for attention to the grate and main steam pipes. Around the same time a partition type screen was installed to the rear of the driving position at No. 1 end and intended to reduce the heat radiating forward into the cab from the smokebox door. Unfortunately its presence made the task of smokebox cleaning even more difficult.

Notification had been received at Eastleigh that the dynamometer car would arrive towards the end of June, and the test staff anticipated undertaking two weeks of trials with 'Leader' during the first half of July following which comparative runs with a Southern 'Mogul' would be made. The route selected was from Eastleigh to Woking and return, allowing for suitable assessment of steaming capabilites over the gradients involved.

However, before these runs could begin the matter of crews had to be resolved, for the reputation of 'Leader' as an unpleasant machine on which to work had reached the ears of the locomen at the nearby running shed who would now be responsible for the test runs. The representative of the loco men on the L.D.C. committee stated that in principle they should have been consulted about the working conditions on 'Leader' and as this had not been the case they felt unable to assist with the tests. The way out of this impasse was for a volunteer crew to work the engine for trial purposes only. So Mr. Townroe as Shed Master posted a notice asking if there were any offers. Two men in the relief gang came forward, Driver Alf Smith and Fireman Sam Talbot, although they did so only on the condition that the runs were made with the slightly cooler No. 2, or bunker end leading. This pair were responsible for all the runs subsequently made from Eastleigh. Indeed if either was not available the engine did not leave the shed. Later both were to receive considerable accolades within the official reports of the runs for they contributed much under what were at times the most extraneous circumstances.

'Leader' and car outside Eastleigh shed. Despite Sam Talbot being the only Eastleigh shed fireman to work the engine on trial, a number of other firemen were detailed to assist in preparation and disposal duties. Few of these men had anything particularly complimentary to say about it.
D. Callender

To test the repairs to the grate and steam pipes a train of 10 coaches totalling 337 tons was taken to Woking on 12.6.50. Even before starting this trial there was a new difficulty and this time no fault of 'Leader'. For in 1950 the Bournemouth line was congested almost to capacity and it was a very difficult proposition to find a suitable spare path in which to run the trials. Consequently the only place available was immediately behind the 5.05 p.m. Bournemouth West to Waterloo passenger train, which on the day in question was in the charge of *Lord Nelson* No. 30852. Therefore, following the Waterloo train clearing the section ahead, Leader pulled smartly out onto the main line and on passing Shawford was said to be going as well as No. 30852; indeed those on board were fearful of a signal check as they were likely to catch up! But such success was short lived for less than one mile further on at Shawford Junction steam pressure began to fall, first to 240 p.s.i. and then to 190 p.s.i. and of course the route was still uphill all the way to Litchfield summit, 17 miles from Eastleigh. Consequently it was necessary for a stop to be made at Micheldever for a 'blow-up'.

After the boiler had rallied sufficiently, the trial continued despite being in official terms deemed a failure because of the enforced stop. At Woking there was a short turnaround after which a long delay occurred waiting for a path for the return run. Arrival back at Eastleigh was not until 2.30 a.m. next morning. The engine worked bunker end first on the up journey and smokebox first on the return.

Investigation at Eastleigh soon located the cause of the poor steaming, a buckled flange plate which meant the smokebox door was drawing air. Accordingly the necessary repairs were effected.

Trials resumed on 15.6.50 but this time with the slightly reduced load of 320 tons. Again steaming difficulties and the need for a 'breather' en-route caused the run to be classified as a failure.

Smith and Talbot had by now a chance to assess the engine for themselves, finding

Head on at No. 1 end and ready to begin the dynamometer car trials. The hole cut into the end was to facilitate connecting the various cables between the engine and test vehicle. This opening had been provided during one of the engines visits to Eastleigh Works when a welder suddenly appeared and proceeded to burn away the metal. 'What are you doing that for . . . ?' asked a bemused worker nearby, 'B------d if I know, I'm just doing what I was told', replied the welder, and picking up his tools he walked away.

Les Elsey

Gradient Profile

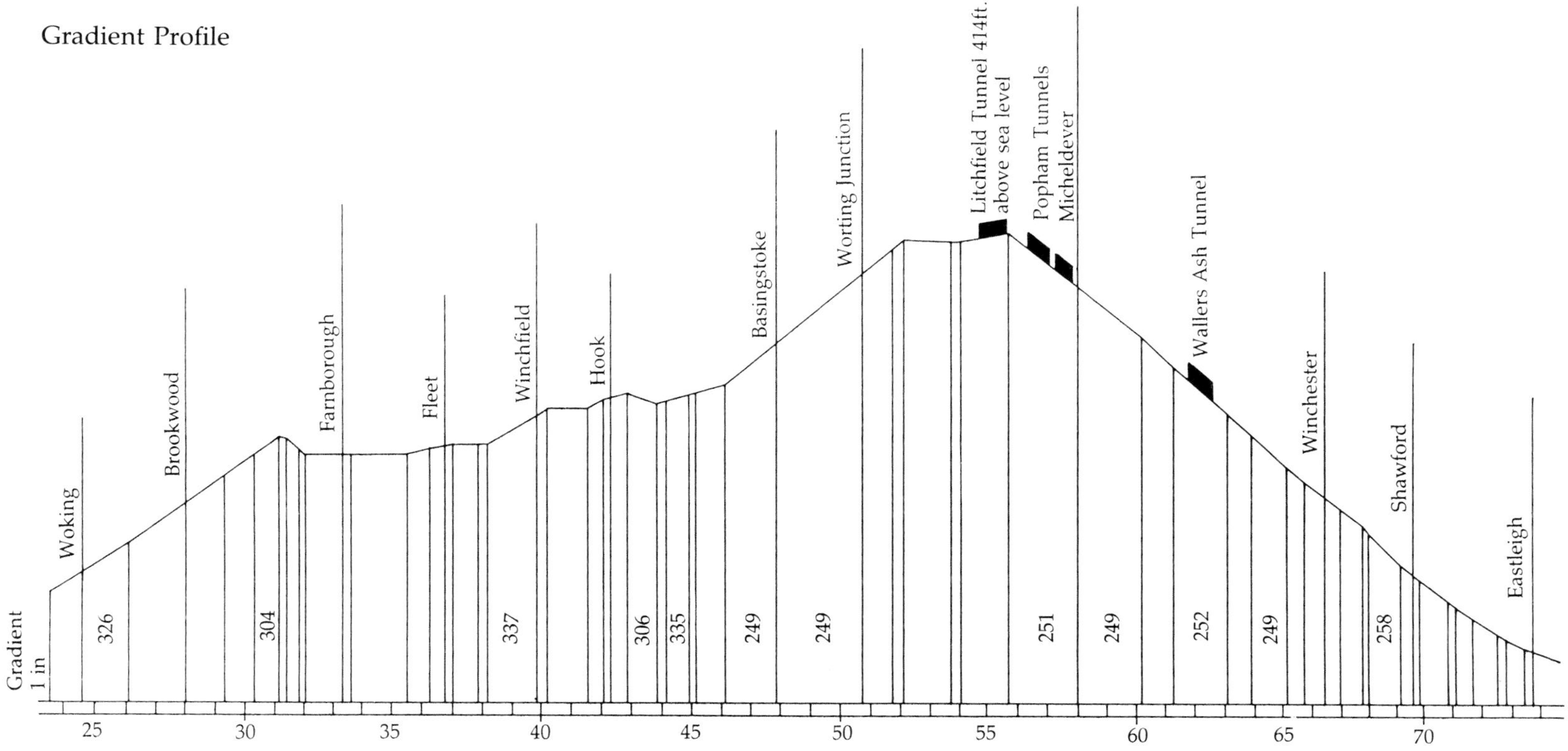

Distances measured from London

The broken crank axle from 'Leader' in Eastleigh works shortly after it was removed from the bogie. A number of reasons were suggested for this failure, including the unsymmetrical drive, lack of movement in the horns, faulty manufacture or even poor design

J. Bell

some of the rumours true and others not so. What was certain was the associated heat and condensation. Much of the former was caused by the injectors beneath the cab of the centre compartment, and the mass of internal pipework within the casing was a continual source of dripping water.

It had been intended for the trips to continue on 19.6.50 but the trial was cancelled and instead the engine entered the works the next day for checking the valve events. At the same time the blast pipe cap was changed and the welding of the boiler examined. What had prompted the examination of the boiler is not recorded. A start was also made towards the fitting of the various items of test equipment needed for the dynamometer car trials.

Because of the sleeve valve design, checking the valve events on 'Leader' was a difficult and time consuming task. As a 'one-off' there was no suitable jig available and so it was necessary to move the engine along an inch at a time with pinch bars. This last task was made slightly easier because of the roller bearings fitted to all the axles and consequently one man could shift the 130+ ton engine by hand with consummate ease.

The dynamometer car, (No. 902532) arrived at Eastleigh on 29.6.50, coinciding with 'Leader' being booked for a further preliminary trial to Woking on eight coaches. This time the trouble began at the start, for on leaving Eastleigh a knocking noise was heard, different from anything else so far experienced and which appeared to be emanating from somewhere on No.1 bogie. Nevertheless for the moment the test continued. But nine miles from the start near Winchester Junction, the noise changed to a deep hammer sound, and appeared to be corresponding with each revolution of the wheels. The

The dynamometer car from the rear. Despite its antiquated appearance this vehicle contained much sophisticated recording equipment and had also been used in the locomotive exchange trials two years previously. It now resides in the National Railway Museum at York.
D. Callender

decision was made to halt the trial at Micheldever and 'Leader' was worked back to Eastleigh as gently as possible.

After the fire had been dropped at the running shed the engine was towed around to the works. Ostensibly this visit was pre-planned as some connections still had to be made with the dynamometer car, but of course the hammer noise had to be investigated. At first it was thought that the right hand valve and cylinder may have fractured but this was soon ruled out and instead attention was concentrated on the centre crank axle. But before this could be examined the body would have to be completely removed and so Brighton were asked to forward the two wooden trestles specially made to support the superstructure. These arrived on 3.7.50, together with an assortment of spares whereupon the bogies were fully removed and the fault at last revealed. The centre crank axle of No. 1 bogie had sheared at one end where the axle joined the wheel.

Not unnaturally there was an immediate call for a check to be made on the same component on No. 2 bogie to see if there were any signs of a similar fault. Tests were also carried out on both crank axles with mechanical and X-ray techniques. Similar results were found on each axle, pointing the conclusions towards a possible design fault rather than any metalurgical defect.

The whole future programme was now in doubt again, for how could the Railway Executive sanction the continuance of trials in the light of the latest findings? Surprisingly Riddles was adamant that the runs must continue as arranged and so instructions were issued for the engine to be fitted with two replacement crank axles and repaired where necessary in order that it might continue running. The replacement parts were taken from those intended for either Nos. 36004 or 36005.

With No. 36001 under repair yet again it was agreed the best course of action was to run the comparative trials with the 'Mogul', a 'U' class 2-6-0, No. 31618 was selected.

Sam Talbot was the fireman on 'Leader' during nearly all the trial runs from Eastleigh. He is shown here some years after the tests in the cab of a Crompton diesel.
Collection of Mrs Talbot

The dynamometer car runs using No. 31618 started on 10.7.50 and ironically only reached Basingstoke, for in the words of the test crew the engine was. '. . . in a poor condition and had amongst its defects a hot left hand trailing axlebox'. Accordingly the run was terminated and No. 31618 returned to Eastleigh for repair.

A different engine of the same class was now chosen, No. 31630 which was successfully modified with test fittings so as to be ready to commence trials by the end of July. No. 31630 was a totally different machine to her sister and performed well from the start. Three return trips between Eastleigh and Woking were completed on consecutive days, the last on 2.8.50. Each run was carried out with due observance to the set 50 mph test limit stipulated for 'Leader' and so the timings were set for an average speed of 40–45 mph. Throughout these and the subsequent runs the test staff were those from the Eastern Region who were given a free hand to conduct the trials in the way their experience dictated. In all cases the coal used was 'South Kirby Hards No. 1' and weighed into 1 cwt bags.

Meanwhile back at Eastleigh repairs progressed steadily on No. 36001, although as some in authority regarded 'Leader' as little more than an unmitigated nuisance there was perhaps not the urgency to the task. Finally by 14.8.50 work was at last completed and steam raised for a light engine trial to Botley the following day. This was again under the charge of the works trials crew. The trip was repeated the following day, a note in the records referring to the fact that some 2,000 gallons of water were used in each direction – a distance of less than five miles.

Another test had been planned for 17.8.50 but it was cancelled as a connecting rod from No. 2 bogie was striking the oil bath. Only minor repairs were needed this time and after a further light engine trial to Fratton on Friday 18.8.50, 'Leader' was moved to the running shed in preparation of the dynamometer car trials to commence after the weekend.

On No. 1 road at Eastleigh during the weekend of 19/20 August 1950 and when final adjustments were being made in preparation for the trials.

D.W. Winkworth

So on Monday 21.8.50 the long awaited trials at last began, No. 36001 steaming away from Eastleigh on a fine summer evening and with eight coaches in tow weighing some 231½ tons. All the trials were again scheduled as evening runs for the reason of line occupancy. In addition to the official observers, a fitter was booked on at the same time as Messrs. Smith & Talbot. The fitter would then assist with any preparations necessary although from the drivers point of view very little needed to be attended to as the use of oil baths and pressure lubrication meant there were only two oiling points on the whole engine.

The official report on the journey reads as follows;

> 'The start from Eastleigh was slow, and the boiler pressure fell quickly from 270 to 210lbs in six minutes, although the regulator was only partially open with 170lbs in the steam inlet pipes. Exhaust pressures of 12 and 12½lbs, and exhaust temperatures of 244 and 246 deg. Farenheit were noted, also a high smokebox vacuum of 5½ inches was recorded. Two minutes later, although the steam chest pressure had fallen to 140lbs. p.s.i. the exhaust temperatures continued to rise to 256 and 280 deg F. and the smokebox vacuum to 7 in. of water. The regulator was eased to give 100 p.s.i. in the steam chest and allow the steam pressure to rise in the boiler. The drawbar arm in ,the dynamometer car indicated unusual vibrations and as the exhaust temperatures continued to rise it was soon evident that all was not well with the engine working. Due to very hard work by the fireman the boiler pressure rose and was maintained at about 240 p.s.i. for the remainder of the journey. Under these conditions the temperature in the firemans cab was abnormal.' – the consequences of the high temperatures are explained in the report of the next run.

Leaving the north yard at Eastleigh and about to join the main line at Allbrook. No. 36001 makes a spirited get away on 21.8.50. Later analysis of the dynamometer car records would show 'Leader' used more oil for lubrication of the motion than a modern diesel used for fuel!
Les Elsey

Upon arrival at Woking the test ended at the south end of the Up yard. The engine and dynamometer car were then detached and the car propelled along the Portsmouth line to Guildford. Both units were then turned individually on the shed turntable and reconnected in anticipation of the return working.

At Guildford Smith and Talbot were able to enjoy a break while the engine was examined. Unfortunately this examination showed the mechanical lubricators of No. 2 bogie to be faulty and so to prevent the likelihood of seizure the test was abandoned with engine and car returning to Eastleigh light the next day.

Following repairs at the works another run was made on 23.8.50 this time with the increased load of 264½ tons.

> 'Prior to starting the up journey from Eastleigh . . . .steam was blowing from the safety valves, but the boiler pressure fell to 185 p.s.i. after 16 minutes. The exhaust pressures were again high and the exhaust temperatures gradually rose to 350 deg. F. which is the limit of the working range of temperature for the indicator in the dynamometer car for this purpose. In order to reduce the coal and water consumption the engine was worked in 20% cut off instead of 30% used on the previous test runs. Although this had the effect of reducing the smokebox vacuum the engine continued to throw burning char from the chimney top. The actual running time was spoilt by a number of signal checks, seven in all, and four signal stops, they assisted in keeping up the boiler pressure. On the return journey from Woking, steam was again blowing from the safety valves and a thicker fire was put on the grate before starting away. The regulator was adjusted to give a maximum steam chest

Shawford, 7.20 p.m., 24.8.50. The headcode signified a main line duty but the legend 'SPL' on the disc indicated a special working. Of all the photographs taken of the engine, both under construction and on test, there are few north of Eastleigh and none at all so far found north of this point.

R. Curl

> pressure and the engine tried out in 15% cut off on the easier sections of the route. This resulted in maintaining a higher boiler pressure and reduced the exhaust steam temperatures within the range of measurement, but there was no improvement in either the coal or water consumption. The engine refused to start on one or two occasions and had to reverse before a drawbar pull of about 5 tons necessary to start the train could be exerted. All the figures and evidence collected at this stage was ample proof that a considerable amount of the steam produced was being wasted, either by leakage past the piston, or sleeve valves of both engine units.'

The last comment was borne out in another way. At Eastleigh the running staff had already experienced difficulties with excessive steam consumption and found an unofficial way to assist matters when the engine was cold. This was simply to run light engine up and down a short length of track a few times which then allowed the cylinders to warm through and hopefully expand the sleeves. Not surprisingly such behaviour was officially frowned upon.

The comments made with regard to the difficulty in starting are most interesting, for they follow almost exactly the problems encountered earlier with No. 2039. On 'Leader' any reluctance to start was overcome by means of the fitter dismounting and then pushing over the reverser with a crow-bar!

Back at Eastleigh in the early hours of 24.8.50, engine and car were again turned and stabled ready for another test later that day. This was to be with 10 coaches equal to 290½ tons.

> 'A fourth test run was made on 24.8.50. When running between Eastleigh motive power depot to the reception sidings to pick up the trainload the cylinder cocks were open to get rid of the condensation. The cylinder of No. 1 end can be seen from the dynamometer car and it was observed that an abnormal quantity of water was issuing from the sleeve valves. The condensed steam was white and oily from the lubrication supply. When attached to the train, the boiler pressure was 275 p.s.i., and again a good thickness of fire was on the firegrate. The weight of the train for this test run was 290½ tons, a light load for an engine of this size. Working in 30% cut off with 140 p.s.i. in the steam chest the boiler pressure fell rapidly to 200lbs. Good work by the fireman got the pressure back to 225lbs but the pressure fell to 140lbs approaching Winchester City, 7½ miles from the starting point, and a running time of 19 minutes. A stop had to be made to regain the boiler pressure but as this so upset the booked path, the test run was abandoned at Micheldever. On arrival back at Eastleigh depot a standing test very clearly showed that steam was blowing to waste and further tests with the engine in this condition was useless.'

Apparently while waiting at Micheldever for the return, an amount of water was taken by means of a ½in. hose connected to a standpipe on the cattle dock – reminiscences of the first run from Brighton.

Back at Eastleigh a decision had once again to be taken on the immediate future and accordingly Riddles was informed of this latest difficulty. The reply though was rapid, ' . . . . the tests must continue . . .', and so again contrary to what had been expected No. 36001 re-entered the works on 28.8.50 with attention focused on valves and pistons.

Three weeks were spent out of service on what involved considerable repairs. On No. 1 bogie a new sleeve was fitted to the left hand cylinder and a number of score marks on the other cylinders smoothed over. Similar repairs were affected to No. 2 bogie, with all the parts again obtained from Brighton and the incomplete engines of the class. In addition, all 144 rings surrounding the sleeves and pistons were renewed (20 on each sleeve and 4 per cylinder) with lesser work also carried out in other areas.

With the engine out of service the testing staff prepared an interim report on the runs so far. (This provides the quotes used in the chapter thus far.)

The engine was eventually released from the works on 20.9.50 and steamed for a light engine trip to Fratton the next day. This was in the charge of Smith and Talbot. The results were very promising and performance reported as '. . . better than at any time in the past.' Upon the return to Eastleigh arrangements were immediately put in hand for the conclusion of the tests, a final check on 22.9.50 revealed for the first time that no defects of any type required attention!

Accordingly on the evening of 25.9.50, No. 36001 left Eastleigh with eight coaches weighing 241½ tons. This was of course less than had been taken in the past, but the intention was to allow the sleeves and rings time to 'bed-in' before attempting a heavier train.

> 'EASTLEIGH – WOKING; The engine was worked mainly in 30% cut off and partial regulator to give 110 to 120lbs in the steam chest. As a result, the train speed rose gradually to 46 m.p.h. on the rising gradients to Litchfield Signal

'U' class 2-6-0 No. 1618 at Salisbury SR shed 20.9.47. Less than two years later as No. 31618 this engine was used in the comparative tests against 'Leader'. For the trials both No. 31618 and her replacement No. 31630 were run with a thin fire and care was taken to avoid undue waste of steam at both the safety valves and injectors. The choice of No. 31618 for comparative trials was itself interesting as she was always regarded as a poor performer and it was hoped the control runs would show up where the deficiencies were.

H.C. Casserley

Box. . . . .On the falling gradients from Basingstoke to Woking, the booked time was maintained, the maximum speed being 55½ m.p.h.'

'WOKING – EASTLEIGH; The engine was worked in 25% cut off with higher steam chest pressures. Signal checks spoilt the running to Brookwood, but with clear signals the steam chest pressure was put up to 200lbs and this gave a drawbar pull of 3.38 tons which accelerated the train from 20 to 41 m.p.h. in 1½ miles. The regulator was eased and at the 31½ mile post, the speed was 50.2 m.p.h. The maximum speed was 54 m.p.h. at mile post 44.'

The following day an extra vehicle was added, making nine in total and equal to 275 tons. As at Brighton any available vehicles were used. For Sam Talbot these runs were far more strenuous than a normal firing turn, his task hampered by the curved coal chute which tended to be anything but self feeding. Fortunately there was always an observer present to assist in moving the weighed bags of coal from the bunker. Even so only one fireman was ever carried per trip, while the number of observers together with the various lumps of scrap placed in the corridor as balance weights made the internal conditions rather cramped. From the fireman's viewpoint it was also difficult for him to gauge exactly where the train was at any time, especially as sound was distorted by the external casing of the engine.

26.9.50. 'EASTLEIGH – WOKING; Working mainly in 25% cut off to Shawford Junction, the speed rose to 42 m.p.h. and the exhaust pressure was up to 14lbs with the result that a good amount of burning char was thrown from the chimney. The gear was changed to 20% cut off, but the exhaust pressure again rose to 14lbs when the speed was 53 m.p.h. When passing through Wallers Ash Tunnel at 53 m.p.h. there was a shower of large pieces of burning char from the chimney top. Sectional running time was maintained to Basingstoke. During the downhill running to Woking, a maximum speed of 56 m.p.h. was noted near Farnborough; this speed could have been exceeded if it had been desirable.

WOKING – EASTLEIGH; The engine put up a good performance by passing Brookwood at 42.5 m.p.h. a drawbar pull of 2.4 tons was maintained and the train speed rose to 50 m.p.h. at mile post 31.

27.9.50. Nine vehicles, equal to 294½ tons.
EASTLEIGH – WOKING; The load was again increased to test the engine when working with higher steam chest pressures. There was some difficulty in obtaining suitable conditions owing to steam blows from the cylinder release valves when the pressure in the cylinders was above 210 p.s.i. At 21 m.p.h., with a steam chest pressure of 195lbs, the drawbar pull was 3.48 tons, drawbar horsepower 872 and the exhaust pressure 15lbs. The boiler pressure gradually fell to 200lbs. The regulator was eased to 130lbs in the steam chest and the boiler pressure rose to 225lbs in three minutes. At this point speed was 51 m.p.h . . .
WOKING – EASTLEIGH: A relatively good performance was made on the continuously rising gradient of 1 in 389 during which the speed rose to 50 m.p.h. in 12 minutes . . . .'

The final trip with the dynamometer car was made on 28.9.50, this time with ten coaches of 325½ tons. From the remarks of the testing staff it was as if some of the steaming difficulties had at last been overcome, although there was still an amount of steam wastage referred to in the blow from the cylinder release valves. Smith and Talbot were also almost used to 'Leader' by now even if they voiced differing views. Alf Smith as driver liked the fact that he could perform his task seated although he was not happy to be separated from his fireman. Sam Talbot however voiced criticism of the working conditions as well as reiterating Smith's earlier comments. The comments made by the crew about being parted from each other should not be read lightly, for they were genuinely concerned as to each others welfare. Had for example 'Leader' ever been involved in an accident and overturned the fireman could well have been trapped. Certainly on all the tests there were always more than just the crew carried.

28.9.50. EASTLEIGH – WOKING; After passing onto the main line at Allbrook, the gear was set at 25% cut off. The speed rose to 50 m.p.h. in 12 minutes and the exhaust pressure rose to 12lbs with a pressure of 195lbs in the steam chest.

WOKING – EASTLEIGH. Special attention is drawn to the particulars of the engine performance from Woking when a speed of 50 m.p.h. was attained in 12 minutes 44 seconds. There was no difficulty in maintaining adequate boiler pressure. During this period 9 cwts of coal were put into the firebox. . . . .'

No doubt because this was the last trial, the engine was allowed more leeway on the return trip. The descent from Litchfield Summit to Eastleigh was taken at far more than the stipulated speed. (Unfortunately we do not know how much more!) Everything performed faultlessly with 'Leader' behaving in the way she had been intended. Back at Eastleigh the dynamometer car and train were uncoupled and the engine taken to the shed. After the fire had been dropped a chain was fastened around the access doors to prevent unauthorised entry. It seemed as if all now depended upon a decision by the Railway Executive.

Engine	No.36001 SR 'Leader' Class (Second Series)							
Train and Route	UP – 6.45 p.m. DOWN – 11.35 p.m.			Eastleigh–Woking Woking–Eastleigh			Special Empty Train	
	UP	DOWN	UP	DOWN	UP	DOWN	UP	DOWN
Date	25.9.50	25.9.50	26.9.50	26.9.50	27.9.50	27.9.50	28.9.50	28.9.50
No. Signal and P. Way Checks	2	6	1	3	4	0	1	0
No. Unbooked stops	1	4	0	2	4	1	1	3
Weight of Engine (in working order) (tons)	130.45	–	–	–	–	–	–	–
Weight of Train behind Drawbar (tons)	241.5	241.5	275.5	275.5	294.5	294.5	325.5	325.5
Train miles (actual)	48.87	49.05	48.825	49.03	48.98	49.03	48.97	49.07
Ton miles (excluding weight of engine)	11800	11840	13450	13500	144200	14440	15940	15970
Ton miles (including weight of engine)	18160	18240	19820	19900	20800	20820	22320	22360
Time booked running min	72	71	72	71	72	71	72	71
Time actual running min	78.45	94.48	71.67	82.15	87.47	74.03	72.98	82.90
Speed mph average	37.35	31.0	40.9	35.8	33.6	39.7	40.25	35.5
Work done h.p. hr	345.8	315.8	402.3	342.2	408.7	324.0	404.33	379.0
Average D.B. pull tons	1.185	1.078	1.380	1.169	1.398	1.105	1.385	1.294
Average D.B. h.p.	264.2	200.5	337.0	250.0	280.5	262.5	332.5	274.5
Coal Total weight lbs	2352	2464	2688	2464	2632	2240	2576	2240
Coal lbs/mile	48.20	50.25	55.00	50.30	53.80	45.70	52.60	45.65
Coal lbs/ton mile (excluding engine)	0.1995	0.2081	0.1997	0.1825	0.1825	0.1551	0.1616	0.1402
coal lbs/ton mile (including engine)	0.1296	0.1351	0.1356	0.1238	0.1266	0.1075	0.1154	0.1002
Coal lbs/hr (running time)	1800	1564	2250	1800	1806	1815	2118	1622
Coal lbs/sq. ft. Grate/hr (running time)	70.6	61.4	88.2	70.6	70.8	71.2	83.0	63.6
Coal lbs/D.B.h.p. hr	6.81	7.81	6.68	7.20	6.44	6.92	6.37	5.91
Water total gall	1807	1712	1927	1807	2000	1635	1987	1929
Water gall/mile	37.0	34.90	39.48	36.88	40.89	33.35	40.60	39.31
Water lbs/ton mile (including engine)	0.996	0.939	0.972	0.908	0.961	0.785	0.890	0.863
Water lbs/hr (running time)	13,820	10,860	16,130	13,200	13,720	13,250	16,340	13,960
Water lbs/sq. ft. heating surface/hr	5.79	4.55	6.76	5.53	5.75	5.55	6.85	5.85
Water lbs/D.B.h.p. hr	52.25	54.25	47.90	52.80	48.95	50.42	49.15	50.9
Evaporation actual lbs water/lb coal	7.68	6.95	7.18	7.33	7.60	7.30	8.61	
Evaporation from and at 212°F	10.17	9.10	9.50	9.54	9.92	9.60	10.16	11.30
Boiler efficiency %	71.9	66.0	67.2	69.1	70.4	71.1	72.0	83.7
Gross calorific value of coal B.Th. U/lb	13,660	13,315	13,660	13,315	13,640	13,055	13,635	13,055
B. Th.Us./D.B.H.P. hr	93025	103,990	91,248	95,868	87,906	90,341	86,855	77,155
Overall efficiency %	2.74	2.45	2.79	2.66	2.90	2.82	2.93	3.3
Weather conditions	Showery		Fine Dry Rail		Showery		Fine Dry Rail	

SUMMARY OF WEIGHINGS No. 36001 PERIOD NOVEMBER 1949 – FEBRUARY 1950

Date	Conditions: Water	Conditions: Coal	No. of weighings		No. 1. (Chimney) Bogie No.1. 1 T. cwt	2 T. cwt	3 T. cwt	No. 2. End. (Water tank) Bogie No.2. 4 T. cwt	5 T. cwt	6 T. cwt	Totals: Bogie No.1 T.c.	Bogie No.2 T.c.	Grand	Increase of weight on right-side: Bogie No.1. T. c	Bogie No.2.	Total
5.11.49 Brighton	Approx 4000 galls	4 tons	1	Right	10 19	13 4	13 14	13 16	15 5	9 9	37 13	38 10	76 7	12 2	8 15	20 17
				Left	11 0	7 0	7 15	6 10	10 6	12 19	25 15	29 15	55 10			
				Total	21 19	20 4	21 9	20 6	25 11	22 8	63 12	68 5	131 17			
16.12.49 Eastleigh	4000 glass + a glass	4 tons	Average of 3	Right	10 19	12 2	10 8	11 14	13 4	11 10	33 9	36 8	69 17	4 15	4 9	9 4
				Left	7 2	10 4	11 8	7 10	11 9	13 0	28 14	31 19	60 13			
				Total	18 1	22 6	21 16	19 4	24 13	24 10	62 3	68 7	130 10			
16.12.49 Eastleigh	200 + galls + ¾ a glass	3 tons	Average of 3	Right	10 10	10 1	10 12	10 11	11 18	8 15	31 3	31 4	62 7	1 5	3 4	4 9
				Left	8 14	10 17	10 7	6 15	8 16	12 9	29 18	28 0	57 18			
				Total	19 4	20 18	20 19	17 6	20 14	21 14	61 1	59 4	120 5			
16.12.49 Eastleigh	Tanks empty glass	Bunker empty	Average of 2	Right	9 18½	11 0½	9 18½	7 14½	8 18½	8 17½	30 17½	25 10½	56 8	1 11	0 8	1 19
				Left	9 4½	8 13½	11 8½	6 7	7 13½	11 2	29 6½	25 2½	54 9			
				Total	19 3	19 14	21 7	14 1½	16 12	19 19½	60 4	50 13	110 17			
2.2.50 Eastleigh	Tanks empty glass	Bunker empty	Average of 3	Right	12 2	9 14	9 15	10 9	9 16	9 1	31 11	29 6	60 17	3 15	5 9	9 4
				Left	7 8	10 8	10 0	7 3	9 13	7 1	27 16	23 17	51 13			
				Total	19 10	20 2	19 15	17 12	19 9	16 2	59 7	53 3	112 10			
2.2.50 Eastleigh	3000 galls + a glass	3 tons	Average of 3	Right	12 7	10 11	10 12	13 0	11 5	11 8	33 10	35 13	69 3	5 18	4 16	10 14
				Left	8 4	10 7	9 1	8 15	11 10	10 12	27 12	30 17	58 9			
				Total	20 11	20 18	19 13	21 15	22 15	22 0	61 2	66 10	127 12			

The Eastleigh weigh-table was capable of registering maximum axle load of up to 25 tons per axle. Apparently when first weighed and before the modifications to the pedestals, the pointers had been forced right off the end of the calibrations. One observer recounting that in his opinion the true weight on one occasion was nearer 30 ton axle maximum. As stated though, this must be taken as an *unconfirmed* report.

Train 6.45 p.m. Eastleigh–Woking
Date: 25.9.50
Record No. 1840.

Particulars of temperatures, pressures, etc.
Engine No. 36001 Southern Region Class 'Leader'

Time	Speed m.p.h.	DB Pull tons Actual	Pressure lbs/sq. in. Steam Chest		Exhaust			S'box Vacuum	Temperatures °F Smokebox		Inlet steam		Exhaust		Reg'r position	Cut off
			No. 1	No.2	No.1	No.2	Boiler	(in.)	A	B	No.1	No.2	No.1	No.2		(%)
6.51	15	1.80	110	100	1	½	230	1½	530	560	435	415	220	220	¼	30
6.54	25	2.66	140	140	5½	5	230	4	580	630	500	490	230	232	¼	30
6.57	35	2.16	115	120	5	5	230	3¾	580	640	540	565	238	240	¼	30
7.01	39	1.81	120	115	7½	5	225	4¾	630	680	560	595	268	246	¼	30
7.03	42	2.04	–	115	–	6½	245	–	–	–	590	620	283	260	¼	30
7.05	45	1.79	110	105	7½	7	235	5	640	690	605	655	322	304	¼	30
7.11	45	1.80	110	110	8¼	8¼	230	5¼	630	690	600	665	348	328	¼	30
7.14	46	1.92	120	120	10	11½	265	5½	660	700	605	670	350*	335	¼	30
7.18	46	1.94	110	110	10	10	245	5½	640	690	605	670	350*	348	¼	30
7.20	52	.80	70	75	4	2¾	240	1	590	640	595	655	350*	350	⅛	15
7.24	20	1.50	–	115	–	¾	220	–	–	–	550	610	350	296	¼	15
7.50	32	2.26	135	140	5¾	4½	225	4	530	565	450	500	296	240	¼	20
7.53	55	1.11	–	80	–	4	250	–	–	–	500	560	310	262	⅛	20
8.00	52	.78	30	60	2½	1¾	240	1½	530	570	505	555	324	278	⅛	20
8.04	50	.80	50	55	3	1¼	250	1½	510	560	510	555	322	276	⅛	20
8.07	51	.98	55	65	4	2	240	2½	540	570	510	555	312	278	⅛	20
8.16	46	1.50	–	95	–	3¾	220	–	–	–	540	570	304	250	¼	20
Averages			98	101	5¾	4¾	236	3½	584	630	540	580	340	280		

No.1 Smokebox End

Positions A. in front of large tubes
B. in front of small tubes.

*Limit of range of instrument in Dynamometer Car.

AN OPPORTUNITY LOST ?

Following the conclusion of the official test runs No. 36001 stood cold and lifeless at the rear of Eastleigh shed awaiting a decision as to her future. To those of Bulleids' former staff who had been involved in the project from its inception it must have seemed as if the result was a foregone conclusion.

Within the Southern Region however there was a school of thought which felt the engine had not yet been given the opportunity to perform in the way in which the design had intended. Therefore, in early October 1950 arrangements were put in hand for what was to be the final series of trials. Before these could be undertaken the engine and boiler were again thoroughly checked and a number of necessary repairs made. These included the renewal of the flexible steam pipes to the generators as well as a number of flange joints connecting the blower and associated components.

As a prelude, a trial run was arranged from Eastleigh to Cosham on 14 October with Messrs. Smith and Talbot once more in charge. All was satisfactory and so the full test was set for three days later on 17 October.

So near and yet so far, No. 36002 in store at Brighton. The engine only required the external covers to the axlebox springs, steam and vacuum pipes and cab windows and she would have been ready for trials. It was said to be just two days work. What is not known is if the modifications carried out to No. 36001 were incorporated in the second engine as the work progressed. If not one could foresee the same problems all over again.

Collection of D. Broughton

No. 36003, No. 1 end, with No. 36002 behind in store at Bognor Regis steam shed, 1.7.50. Officially both engines were moved here because of a shortage of storage space at Brighton, but it may also have been an attempt to remove the project from the public gaze. Nos. 36002 and 36003 had also spent a period in store at New Cross, Gate Shed, London. Both were finally cut up at Brighton.
Collection of D. Broughton

On the day of the actual run No. 36001 was coupled up to 13 coaches weighing 430 tons and with the route the same as for the previous dynamometer car trials, viz Eastleigh to Basingstoke–Woking and Guildford returning the same way. Again Smith and Talbot crewed, with in addition a senior member of the Railway Executive on board, Roland Bond. One observer who witnessed the departure described the start as '. . . effortless . . .', a most interesting comment bearing in mind that this start was with in excess of a 100 tons greater trailing load compared with anything attempted on previous trials.

Unfortunately such good fortune was not destined to continue, for at the customary Basingstoke water stop the engine refused to move either forward or back and some six minutes were wasted attempting to draw up to the water column. Such eccentricies of behaviour were hardly likely to impress Mr Bond. The remainder of the run was without incident, the return working south of Basingstoke achieved at a speed much greater than anything so far obtained. It was almost as if 'Leader' herself was trying to make up for its earlier misdemeanour at Basingstoke.

The official record of the run however contained a certain amount of criticism;

> 'The engine ran satisfactorily and whilst some time was lost on the easier sections, this could well have been avoided by slightly heavier working. The steam pressure and water level were fairly well maintained, but steaming was not entirely satisfactory during the heaviest working conditions. The performance of the locomotive was such, however, as to indicate that a trial could be attempted with 480 tons.'

No. 36004 in embryo form and consisting just of main frames and boiler. The coach bogies were merely to allow the components to be moved around the yard area. Nos. 36004/5 had not reached anywhere near the stage of construction of the other engines, both little more than a collection of parts which were robbed to provide spares for No. 36001. Both Nos. 36004/5 were eventually taken away for disposal in goods waggons.

W.N.J. Jackson

Leader was being given one last chance to redeem herself and 2 November was the date set for what was to be the final test. Again the same crew were in charge on the same route.

Coupled to no less than 15 coaches, amounting to some 480 tons No. 36001 left Eastleigh in the early November gloom heading north. The only concession made was an extra 5 min. in the passing time to Winchester Junction and considered necessary because of the heavy load to be hauled unaided on the long climb from Eastleigh.

This time there was no senior observer, but such was the performance of the engine that 50 mph was maintained almost throughout, while at Micheldever the safety valves lifted indicating too much steam was available. Passing Worting the train was ½ minute early although a signal stop meant arrival at Basingstoke was a little delayed. An official account of the run to this point referred to the performance thus;

> 'The performance on this test was far in excess of anything previously attained, the estimated power output corrected for gradient, being of the order of 1100 h.p. at the drawbar. Steam temperatures were not taken due to the failure of the instrument.'

Certainly all on board must have looked forward to the remainder of the run. But it was not to be, for while taking water the opportunity was taken for a check around the engine where it was found that the smokebox door was slightly ajar. Had the demands for steam not previously been so prolific this would probably have mattered little, but as it was the power output obtained had caused an amount of cinders and char to fall out of the door and which now threatened to set the wooden lagging and floor alight, whilst

The incomplete No. 36003 at Brighton. A considerable amount of work was needed on this engine before it would have been ready for steam trials. She is shown being shunted by the Brighton works shunter at the latter location on 23.5.51 and just before final cutting up. Work on the 'Leader' class and specifically Nos. 36002/3 was responsible for the delay in completing Nos. 34091–94 a batch of 'Light Pacifics' at Brighton. The Pacifics not appearing in traffic until the Autumn of 1949 several months later than had originally been intended.
Collection of D. Broughton

the door itself was badly warped. There was then no alternative but to abandon the test and return to Eastleigh, No. 36001 leaving her train in the sidings at Basingstoke and heading south for Eastleigh light engine.

Even so it was not quite over, as speed was again worked up to a very high rate, some reports speak of as much as 90 mph and without a hint of trouble from any quarter, indeed the engine rode as smoothly as a coach. Upon arrival at Eastleigh it transpired that the failure was simply due to human error, a workman who had omitted to ensure the smokebox door was secure before the engine had left the shed. Even so all that was required was a replacement smokebox door and a number were available from the unfinished sisters to No. 36001. But it was not to be and with her fire dropped, No. 36001 was shunted to an empty siding alongside the shed, she would never steam again.

Bulleid himself was by now well ensconsed as Chief Mechanical Engineer to the C.I.E. in Eire and so could only receive reports on No. 36001 via members of his former Southern staff. As previously stated Riddles had also dictated that work on No. 36001's sister engines be suspended, Nos. 36002–5 were stored in various stages of completion. This fact too was communicated to Bulleid, which almost certainly led to a small delegation of officials from the Irish Railways visiting Brighton with a view to purchasing the incomplete machines.* However, nothing further come of the visit.

* Recorded in correspondance between the writer and the late Don Bradley author of several books on locomotives.

'Leader' on trial and awaiting departure from Brighton Station. The engine never worked any revenue earning trains and so the choice of commencing tests from the passenger station was to simulate realistic operating conditions. This was the photograph reproduced in the American journal, *Mechanical Engineering* with the caption. '. . . Leader class engine in service'. The alternating light and dark patches on the side sheeting is thought to be accentuated by side lighting.

National Railway Museum

CC1 the Irish Turf Burner, awaiting the cutters torch at Inchicore in 1963. The similarity with the original 'Leader' design is obvious and it was to fail for reasons of politics. Some lessons though had been learnt, for the boiler was placed centrally about the chassis and with a joint compartment for the driver and fireman. The 'engine' units too were improved and removable from the power bogies.

Colin Boocock

Was Bulleid then intent on producing a new 'Leader'? indeed he was, with the first hint of this in an article in the journal *Mechanical Engineering* (1950) under the title 'Locomotive and Rolling Stock Developments in Great Britain.'

The article set out to show how steam locomotive development had taken place, with obvious preference given to Bulleid's own achievements. A detailed description was given of 'Leader' and included several photographs. One of these showed the prototype about to depart from Brighton with a test train and the slightly misleading caption of 'Leader class engine in service.'

The text which was obviously written before the final runs with No. 36001 included;

> 'While in American eyes this is a small engine, its horsepower will be about 1700 and consequently it will give as good results as a Diesel-Electric locomotive with a 2000 h.p. engine. How successful we have been in the new design remains to be seen, but the new features in the engine should give us better service, help to improve the performance of the steam locomotive and restore steam traction to favour.'

A few sentences after there is a direct clue as to the future direction of Bulleid's work and which with hindsight may be taken to include the knowledge that No. 36001 was already doomed even before publication of the official BR report;

> 'While in this Leader class of engine the developments of the steam locomotive has been carried a stage further, there is still much work to be done. The use of the blast to create draft should give way to fans so that we can control the production of steam accurately. The exhaust steam should not be allowed to escape to the atmosphere but should be returned to the boiler. Experimental work already done encourages the thought that these two problems can be solved, and I commend them to the young engineers as worthy of investigation. I shall feel more than recompensed if I have shown that while the Stephenson locomotive may in some circumstances be dead or dying, this cannot be said of steam traction itself. If new designs be developed in the light of our present greater knowledge and the servicing of the locomotive be brought up to date – in short, if only we can demolish the conservatism which is destroying the steam locomotive rather than give up any of its customary ways – then we can look forward to a revival of steam traction.'

But what was Bulleid trying to say, was it a vindication of the existing 'Leader' design or a veiled hint towards another progression of steam or perhaps another new 'Leader'? In fact it was probably both, for he was already formulating the ideas which were to develop into the Irish turf burning engine and which was in effect Leader Mk. 2.*

In the meantime on the Southern Region the report of the dynamometer car tests, including the comparative runs against the 'U' class engine had been published. As was expected there was considerable criticism of the design which was hardly surprising after the number of problems that had occurred. (Extracts from the report are reproduced as Appendix D.)

But what the dynamometer car did not do was draw any positive conclusions and

* The Turf Burner is described briefly in Appendix I.

Forlorn and lifeless, No. 36001, the only 'Leader' to steam on trials awaiting the cutters torch at Eastleigh in 1951. Bulleid is reputed to have said that had the engine been intended for use on other railways then water pick-up gear and more coal would have been carried. Many years later Robin Riddles, the former BR Chief Mechanical Engineer when interviewed said about Bulleid, 'As a man I liked him and we got on well, but he was an individualist who wanted to do it his own way, and some of what he did was questionable. I couldn't fathom some of his thinking.' When asked about the decision to scrap 'Leader' he continued, 'It was the only sensible decision to make. The thing was 30 tons overweight, and the boiler so badly balanced it needed 2½ tons of pig-iron on one side to balance it up. Apart from that, the fireman was forced to stand so close to the firebox he was burning himself. The fireman had to lag himself with sandbags to deflect the heat. Was there a job for Bulleid after Nationalisation? – No, how could there be. Having been king of his own dungheap, how could he suddenly come and serve in mine? The surprise to me was that having failed on the Southern, he went to Ireland and failed there too.'
Lens of Sutton

instead this was left to R.A. Riddles in his memorandum to the Railway Executive dated 20 November 1950.

The report dealt with the progression of the tests to date as well as the various remedies attempted in an effort to overcome problems. – see Appendix H. Midway through came the first damning statement;

> 'There are only two alternatives which now present themselves in respect of the future of this class of locomotive. They are;
>
> a) To make a number of major modifications to the present design with a view to overcoming the difficulties which have been experienced and the deficiencies which have been revealed.
>
> or:–
>
> b) To scrap the locomotive so far completed and the other four in varying stages of construction.'

1-Co-Co-1 Diesel Electric No. 10201 passing Basingstoke with the 1.0 p.m. Waterloo–Exeter express, 29.3.55. All three of these Southern diesels used the same body to bogie mounting as on 'Leader' which gave trouble-free service throughout their lives. Later still the BR class 40, 45 and 46 diesels would adopt a similar mounting. Bulleid was of course principally a steam man and although the body shell and underframe of the diesel were to his own design, the internal mechanisms were not. The body profile matches well with the design of his coaches behind. These engines were popular with their crews for they sported a hot plate, wash basin and lavatory for the crew, enabling both driver and fireman to go home clean from a shift.

P.J. Kelley

The various changes required in accordance with option (a) were then listed in detail – again see Appendix H, after which came the final judgement.

> 'Expenditure amounting to £178,865 has already been incurred. So far it has not been possible, nor will it be possible to place this locomotive in revenue earning service without further heavy expense. I have not estimated what this further expense might be because, even if it were incurred and all the defects eliminated the locomotive, as modified, would offer no advantages compared with one of conventional well-tried design.
>
> I am compelled, therefore to RECOMMEND that the second alternative namely, the completed locomotive and the the four in various stages of construction, should be scrapped and that the authority for their construction as part of the 1948 Locomotive Building Programme should be cancelled.'

In just two brief paragraphs 'Leader' was effectively killed off. But the question remains was it the right decision to make? Faced with this evidence Riddles had no other choice at that time. The railways had insufficient funding to develop such a radical new steam design whilst it was already recognised in 1950 that steam as the prime mover was to be eliminated as soon as possible.

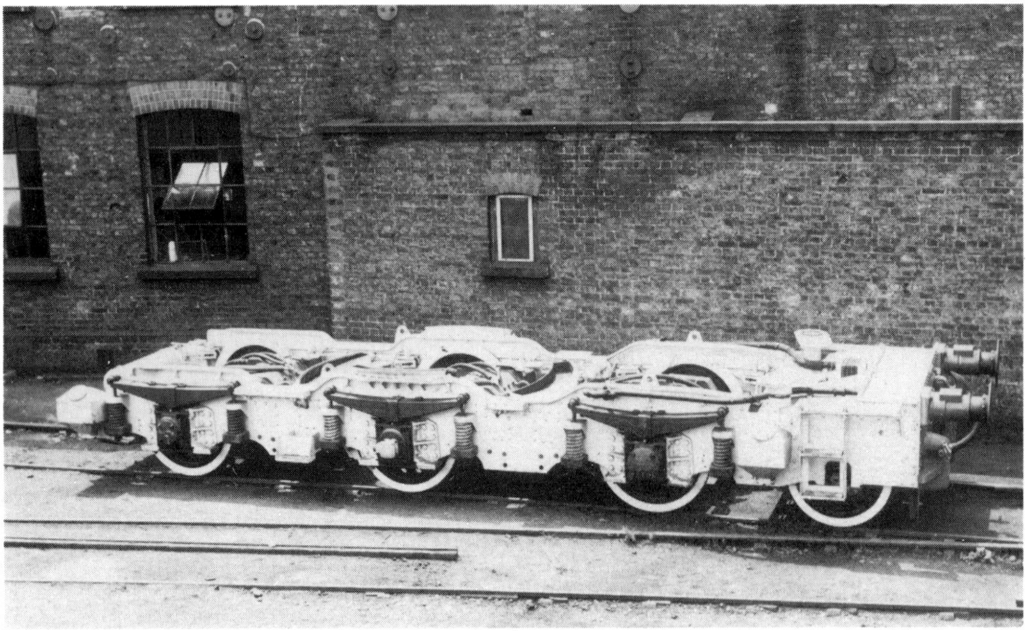

The centre pivotless bogie for diesel electric No. 10202 outside Ashford Works in June 1951. The body mounting pads can be discerned on either side of the centre driven axle.
Les Elsey

This may at first appear strange, especially as in 1950 all four regions were still building steam engines to pre-nationalisation designs and the final range of BR standard designs were still to emerge. However, with thought the reasons become clearer, what was needed was a range of conventional 'go anywhere, cope with anything' designs as indeed the 'Standards' would become. 'Leader' just did not fit in.

Back at Eastleigh No. 36001 still languished alongside the shed, its sister engines towed away from the public eye into store, first at New Cross, then Bognor Regis before returning to Brighton and the cutters torch. The pioneer No. 36001 remained in the open until the evening of 25 April 1951 when she was towed to the adjacent Eastleigh Works for cutting. A few weeks later most of the engine had been completely dismantled although parts from the bogies remained by the works oil store for several years.

It was hoped to utilise the roller bearings from the 'Leader' engines for the centre axles of the 'Q1' class, but in the event the amount of modification that would have been required meant such a consideration had to be abandoned.

Quietly BR no doubt believed the whole project could be quickly forgotten, but the railway press refused to be silenced as per a correspondent for the *Railway Gazette* on 25 May 1951 who asked;

> 'I wonder if an appeal could be made through your columns for more information about this design? I know of no official information or photographs published about this interesting class although it is now two years since the first one appeared from Brighton Works. (As can be seen within the text numerous official views WERE taken of 'Leader' and contemporary documentary evidence recorded. – KJR.) As far as my information goes only one 'Leader' class locomotive has ever been steamed and that has been lying out of use in the open at Eastleigh since early November. If this locomotive

The principles of 'Leader', a BR Mk. 6 bogie and with the same damping and cushioning arrangement as on 'Leader'.

Ian Shawyer

design is unfortunately unsuccessful there may be an attempt in official quarters to forget that it ever existed as has happened in the past with some experimental designs. It seems odd that the extensive trials with this locomotive should appear to have been abandoned just when they appeared to be meeting with a fair measure of success. The locomotive apparently made several quite successful runs to Woking about last October.'

The reply from BR was curt;

'. . . . for varying technical reasons the experiments with the prototype 'Leader' class locomotive were not as satisfactory as had been hoped and to obviate the expense which would be involved in continuing them for a problematical return, it has been decided not to proceed further with this novel design.'

As such BR decreed the matter was closed, any further attempt by outside individuals to glean more information was either politely refused or stone-walled against the harshness of officialdom.

Such an attitude no doubt contributed to the aura surrounding the engine which consistantly refused to subside. It finally culminated in the dramatic revelations of the *Sunday Dispatch* on 18 January, 1953, however true investigative journalism had given way to inaccurate sensationalism.

Sunday Dispatch

152nd Year. No. 7,889. 2½d. JANUARY 18, 1953. Radio Page 6

£500,000 Wasted On Three Useless Engines

RAILWAYS' BIGGEST FIASCO

They Tried To Hush It Up

By Sunday Dispatch Reporter

THREE huge railway engines, which cost altogether about £500,000 to build, now lie rusting and useless in sheds and sidings—silent and hidden evidence of the biggest fiasco produced by Britain's nationalised railways.

One of the Leader class locomotives.

This situation comes to light as the result of *Sunday Dispatch* inquiries, prompted by the threatened increase in fares and allegations of mismanagement on the railways.

The engines, 67ft.-long monsters of the Leader class, with driving cabins at each end were built in 1948 and 1949 to "revolutionise" rail travel.

They were part of a £750,000 experiment undertaken by Mr. O. V. Bulleid, chief mechanical engineer, of British Railways, Southern Region.

I can reveal that the region's officials regard the experiment as one of their biggest failures.

It was a failure that had been hushed up.

From the start the plan to build Mr. Bulleid's dream loco was kept secret.

But news leaked out late in 1948, when the designer gave the British Association some details of "a revolutionary steam locomotive."

The first of the Leaders, known to railwaymen as No. 36001, was then being built at the Southern Region works in Brighton. It started its trials in 1949, and work began immediately on the other two.

Towed Back

From start to finish the "revolutionary" gave trouble. Workers at the Eastleigh (Hants) sheds frequently saw No. 36001 being towed back for repair by an "old fashioned" engine.

Firemen who worked aboard her during the test period reported the Leader was the most uncomfortable loco on the track.

Ventilation in the centre portion, where they stoked in a corridor running between the two driving cabins, was very poor.

One worker told me: "We all knew the three Leaders as 'The White Elephants.' Some who had ridden in them used less polite descriptions.

"Frequently the 'Flying Tramcar,' as others called her, broke down.

Two In One

Women In Prison

GODFREY WINN'S GREATEST SERIES

By The Editor Of The SUNDAY DISPATCH

FOR one hour yesterday, I sat enthralled as Godfrey Winn told me about one of the most remarkable experiences he has ever had in all his crowded, colourful life. He had just spent an entire day—from early morning to late at night—in Britain's most famous prison for women—Holloway.

He had talked to the prisoners, eaten their kind of meals, saw how they lived, how they dressed, where they slept. He talked over their problems with them and with the Governor and other officials of Holloway. Even the mothers whose babies were born during their sentence talked frankly and freely to Godfrey Winn.

HE WAS ABLE TO SEE AND DO ALL THIS BECAUSE HE HAS BEEN GIVEN A PRIVILEGE RARELY, IF EVER, GRANTED TO A WRITER—OFFICIAL PERMISSION TO VISIT EVERY TYPE OF WOMEN'S PRISON IN GREAT BRITAIN IN ORDER TO FIND OUT FOR HIMSELF THE TRUTH ABOUT THE CONDITION AND LIFE OF THE WOMEN WHO ARE KEPT IN BRITAIN'S JAILS.

Many sensational, highly coloured stories have been written about women's prisons, but Godfrey Winn's report will give the world the plain, unvarnished truth.

It is more gripping than any fanciful account could be.

The facts he has gathered in the course of his investigation will interest every reader of the* SUNDAY DISPATCH *as much as they interested me.

'ARISTOCRACY DOOMED AND DAMNED'

Shinwell Outburst Over The Coronation Plans

A FORMER Socialist Minister of Defence and Secretary of State for War, Mr. Emanuel Shinwell, yesterday attacked Coronation arrangements.

He said, at Halesowen, Worcestershire, that he had the highest respect for the young Queen and wished her long life and a successful reign. But when he read that the standard-bearers at the Coronation were all from the aristocracy, and particularly from the military, he wondered at it all.

We were in a democratic age and wanted this age to usher in an era of peace.

What more appropriate than that the Queen should be accompanied by her friends and by those who represented the scientific world, the medical profession, the nurses, miners, farm-workers, steel-workers, the railwaymen.

They were the salt of the earth

FARES-RISE NOW MAY BE QUERIED AT WESTMINSTER

Winner Of T
First Heat In T
1953 National Ba
ing Beauty Cha
pionship Is He
Patricia Camer
Aged 20, A Cashi
Of Glasgow.

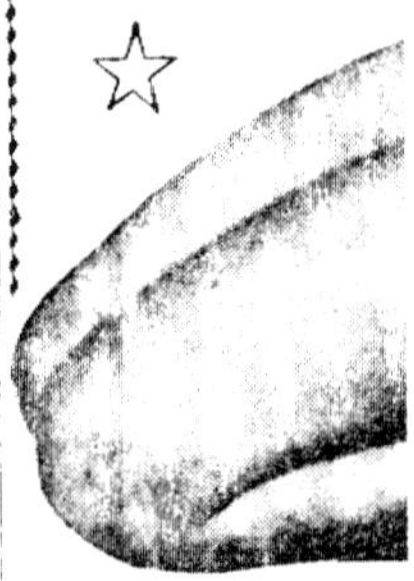

Police A... To Fre... On Thef...

A MAN who had sworn he w... crime for which he had ... was released from prison yes... tion to get his bail reduced.

"Information has come to ... earlier, would have resulted ... detective-sergeant told the ...

ALARM OVER 'LOST' MAILBAG THAT WASN'T LOST AFTER ALL

By Sunday Dispatch Reporter

THE Mystery of the Missing Mailbag of Reading Station was solved late last night.

But only after detectives and ...

Extract from the *Sunday Dispatch* newspaper.

Boiler and firebox from No. 36001 after removal for scrap. The firebox ribs are clearly visible with the side sheets partly cut through and ready for removal. The evidence of heat distortion is quite remarkable.
Collection of B. Curl

The next day the *Daily Telegraph* printed a more accurate assessment but its circulation was unlikely to reach the same numbers of the populace as the sunday newspaper. The damage had been done, and BR were now on the defensive and with any reference to Leader ignored whenever possible.

Meanwhile over in Ireland Bulleid astonished his critics by saying, '. . . . we will probably do something of the sort over here', but by now the news value of the project had dimmed and few heard such comments. Those in the know however were well aware that this was a further reference to the 'Turf Burner', one may perhaps only wonder about the thoughts of the Irish Railway officials!

Subsequently little reference was made to 'Leader' for some years. However, despite the actual locomotive having ceased to exist, aspects of its design were to be resurrected, ironically by the very group that had condemned it, BR.

The pivotless bogie for example appeared under 'Leader', then the three Southern main line diesels and finally the first generation of main line diesel-electrics, Class 40, 45 & 46. Similarly in 1967 the dashpot damping system was used by the Southern Region for its 90 mph electric sets on the Bournemouth Electrification scheme. These were in both cases a direct descendant of 'Leader' principles, but not referred to by BR as such.

Regretfully little else of the design found a place in future developments, the superb steam raising capacity of the boiler, the full weight available for adhesion, the symmetrical and continually even drive, none were used in the final progression of steam. Neither it would seem were any of Bulleid's ideas used for further progression in steam engine design.

So was it all a waste, in terms of time, effort and finance? With regard purely to cost the answer must be in the affirmative but with regard to other areas there is no clear cut answer.

Certainly Bulleid had tried to point the way forward. The problem really comes down to a matter of timing and, in this respect, the onset of nationalisation meant that No. 36001 was really condemned before she ever turned a wheel. It would have required a faultless performance from the outset to alter this. In the form No. 36001 took, the timing of her birth would never have been right, she was a hybrid and in essence stillborn.

But why such controversy over what was really a relatively small amount of money? Especially when the chapters of history are littered with similar engineering feats, TSR2, the on–off progress of the Channel Tunnel and more recently the Advanced Passenger Train. If we learn from the experience of others then the concept of these projects is not lost; if not we too are the losers. The time was never right for 'Leader', CC1, the 'Irish Turf Burner' came nearer to the ideal but still failed to perform exactly as needed and anyway by then it was already too late. Could it be that we failed 'Leader', rather than it failed us?

TEST OF 17 OCTOBER 1950

Place	Time Bkd. p.m.	Time Actual p.m.	Pressure Boiler	Pressure Stm. ch.	Cut off %	Water in glass (F= 6½)	S'box vac. (in. of water)	Temp °F lge. tubes	Temp °F small tubes	Remarks
Eastleigh	6.45	6.45	260	145	67	Full				
				140	15					
Allbrook		6.51¼	250	200	30	Full	4½	620	600	Engine worked very
			260	230	"		8	700	630	lightly to
			245	"	15		6½	"	"	Allbrook Jc
Shawford		6.57	240	"	18	5in.	8	"	640	and mainly
Shawford Jc.			225	220	"		8	710	635	due to this
										5 min. lost to
St. Cross Tunnel			"	"	"		8½	"	"	Winchester Jc.
Winchester		7.1¼	230	225	20	4in.	9	740	680	Showers of sparks from
Winchester Jc.	6.59	7.4	"	220	"	2½in.	"	750	700	chimney about 20%
										being alight on reaching
			235	225			9	760	730	ground. 15 mph PWS
Wallers Ash Box			250	240	20	2½in.	4	660	620	
Weston Box			240	235	"	2in.	7	720	680	
Micheldever		7.14½	220	205	"	2in.	8	720	685	B.P. & Water in glass
Litchfield Tunnel			185	160	"	2in.	6	715	675	not maintained
Worting Jc	7.19	7.23	200	60	"	2½in.				
Basingstoke	7.24	7.27	6 minutes taken to get engine set for taking water							
	7.32	7.32	260	130	67	2in.				
			255	160	15		4	630	580	
Hook		7.46½	240	135	"	1½in.	5	670	630	
Winchfield		7.49	230	120	"	1¼in.	4	665	625	
Fleet		7.55¼	230	120	"	1¼in.	5	650	610	
Farnboro'		7.55¼	230	120	"	1¾	"	645	600	
Brockwood		8.1	210	200	"					
Woking	8.5	8.3¼								To local line
										Sig. checks

TEST OF 2 NOVEMBER 1950

Place	Time		Pressure		Cut Off	Water in glass	S'box vac.	Temp °F		Remarks
	Bkd. p.m.	Act. p.m.	Blr.	Stm. Ch.	(%)	(F = 6½)	(in. of water)	Lge. tubes	small tubes	
Eastleigh	6.40	6.40	260	240	67	F	1	500	500	Started without difficulty
			270	130	25	..	1¾	600	585	
Allbrook Jc.	6.45	6.45½	245	240	10	..	2½	650	620	Pricker & dart used
			260	255	18	..	4	680	630	
Shawford		6.53½	230	225	..	..	6½	730	680	
Shawford			220	210	..	..	7	730	660	Pricker used
St. Cross Tunnel			..	..	..	..	..	..	..	
Winchester		6.58¾	245	240	..	..	9	750	700	.. ..
Winchester Jc.	6.59	7.1¾	255	225	..	..	10½	760	710	
Wallers Ash Box		7.5	245	220	..	..	..	750	700	Pricker & dart used
Weston Box		7.7	240	225	..	..	10	..	720	.. ..
Micheldever		7.9½	250	235	..	5½in.	..	785	750	
			260	250	20	5in.	13½	800	780	
Lichfield Tunnel		7.12½	255	240	..	4in.	..	820	800	
Worting Jc.	7.19	7.18½								Pricker used.
Basingstoke	7.24	7.26								Sig. stop 1½ min.

	17 October 1950	2 November 1950
Load (tons)	430	480
Coal (total) (cwt)	52½	22 (Eastleigh–Basingstoke only)
lbs/mile	59.6	–
llbs/mile (Eastleigh–Basingstoke only)	86.0	94.8
lbs/D.B.h.p. hr*	6.5	6.4
lbs/sq. ft. grate/hr (Eastleigh–Basingstoke only)	125	130
Water (total) gall	3570	1834 (Eastleigh–Basingstoke only)
gall/mile	37.4	–
gall/mile (Eastleigh–Basingstoke only)	55.0	70.5
lbs/D.B.h.p. hr*	41.0	51.0
lbs/hr (Eastleigh–Basingstoke only)	19,000	24,500

* Figures for 17 October refer to the complete trip Eastleigh to Woking and return. Figures for 2 November have been assessed from these on the basis of comparative coal and water figures for Eastleigh–Basingstoke.

APPENDIX A

THE PAGET LOCOMOTIVE

Sir Cecil Paget was Works Manager at Derby on the Midland Railway during the period 1904–1909. During this time he designed a 2-6-2 tender engine of larger dimensions than many of the machines then running on the MR with the intention of avoiding much of the double heading then necessary.

Externally there was much that was in keeping with the aesthetic Midland style, but within the engine there were incorporated eight single acting cylinders 18in. x 12in. stroke and with steam distribution by sleeve valves.

Paget's reasons for the use of sleeve valves were believed to come from the time he was an engineering student and in addition the success of a similar stationary engine installed in the power house at Derby Works.

The only known photograph of the Paget engine, with its origins in contemporary Midland design very apparent. What Paget and Bulleid failed to realise was that a sleeve valve engine would only work well when run at a constant speed. Most successful sleeve valve engines adopted this principle. The same principle occurred with dry firebox sides, they were ideal on a stationary machine but subjected to the vibration of a railway environment it was impossible to keep the bricks in position. Ironically another parallel was when it came to photographing the engine, for any attempt to do so whilst the Paget engine was at Derby was prohibited. Years later when 'Leader' was at Eastleigh a railway employee found photographing the machine had his film destroyed.

British Railways

The design also incorporated a dry back firebox with semicircular water jacket on top. The curved sides of the firebox were lined with firebricks of varying thickness. For this reason the firebox was wider than normal and in consequence the design was itself changed from a 4-6-0 to a 2-6-2 to provide for a greater space.

Reputedly the engine ran well and attained a speed in excess of 80 mph. In addition it seemed suitable for almost any type of duty.

Unfortunately, the politics within the Midland Railway were against the design regardless of any promise it showed, and with Paget himself removed from the position of Works Manager to Superintendant of the Traffic Department he was unable to continue with what was in reality a private design. Much of this was also because he could not provide sufficient private funds and the MR would not assist sufficiently.

Failures did occur, with both the lining of the firebox dry sides and also with the valve gear which was difficult to keep steam tight and free of seizure. When problems arose on the road the delays to other traffic did nothing to assist Paget's cause.

Given the number 2299, the engine ran trials to various destinations including Leicester. By 1913 it was in store at Derby and covered over by a sheet in the paint shop. It was scrapped in 1915.

Probably the best account of this machine was published in a booklet produced by the *Railway Gazette* in 1945 and can now be obtained to order at most libraries.

APPENDIX B

SOUTHERN RAILWAY AND SOUTHERN REGION LOCOMOTIVE STOCK

New and Withdrawn 1941–1951

	New	Withdrawn
Year ending		
31.12.41	6 MN	1
21.12.42	4 MN 40 Q1	2
21.12.43		9
21.12.44	2 MN	22
21.12.45	8 MN 20 WC	5
21.12.46	32 WC	24
21.12.47	19 WC 14 USA	44
21.12.48	8 MN 19 WC	71
21.12.49	2 MN 11 WC	90
21.12.50	9 WC	48
21.12.51	1 WC	204
Totals	194 additions	520 withdrawals

Nos. 36001–5 are not included in the above totals.

Locomotives on loan are also not included. In 1947 there were 30 Ministry of Supply 2-8-0 engines on the SR.

Engines withdrawn include members of the A12, K10, Paddlebox, F1, B1, B4, B4X, J, T1, Atlantics and large wheeled 0-6-2T classes.

During the war years few engines had been condemned. The years immediately afterwards involved condemnation of types overdue for withdrawal.

Commencing in 1951 there was a mass withdrawal of the smaller 4-4-0 classes, particularly as the influx of LMS tank engines and BR Standard types began to take effect. Both these types are not shown in the new totals.

APPENDIX C

Extracts from *Modern Transport* 26.10.47. 'New Conception of Steam Locomotive Design – Lessons for the Immediate future'.

O.V. Bulleid

'In the early days of railways the locomotives were purchased from outside builders and the railway company was content to operate them and allow them to be maintained by the builder . . . . In order that the repairs could be done economically the necessary machine tools and other equipment were provided gradually and it was soon appreciated that this equipment was equally suited in manufacturing new locomotives.

. . . . it will inevitably be suggested that the accepted methods of design or construction cannot be expected to give substantially better results. That is to say, the results were as good as could be expected with the designs, materials, finish, and methods of operation which were used. Consequently if we are to reach the higher level of achievement in continuity of service, which is now required, a new conception of the steam locomotive is also needed.

Such thoughts caused us to question the accepted ideas and forced us to investigate the locomotive as regards, (1) design, (2) use and (3) servicing. The very age of the steam locomtive has acted against its further development for its bad features have come to be accepted as inherent and inevitable. It is these bad features which enable other forms of transport to compete with it and consequently such features must be eliminated if the steam locomotive is to survive. Our investigations soon satisfied us there that was room for improvement under all three heads . . . .

. . . . What sort of locomotive may we expect to see if it is to meet the majority of our future requirements? . . . . The locomotive should be built (1) to be run over the majority of the company lines; (2) to be capable of working all classes of train up to 90 mph; (3) to have its whole weight available for braking and the highest percentage thereof for adhesion; (4) to be equally suited for running in both directions without turning with unobstructed look-out; (5) to be ready for service at short notice; (6) to be almost continually available; (7) to be suited for complete 'common use'; (8) to run not less than 100,000 miles between general overhauls with little or no attention at the running sheds; (9) to cause minimum wear and tear to the track; and (10) to use substantially less fuel and water per drawbar horsepower developed. . . .

. . . A new type of Southern engine has been designed, the construction of five has been authorised. The engine will incorporate the following features and it is hoped will satisfy the design criteria given above. The locomotive is carried on two six wheeled bogies, the general design of which follows that of the bogies I designed for use under the company's electric locomotives. . . . The engine develops a torque the uniformity of which is comparable with that of a nose suspended electric traction motor but has a higher speed range and the unsprung weight is less. The capacity of the boiler has been made greater, relative to the cylinder horsepower than in the case of any previous Southern locomotive. The cabs at the ends will give an improved lookout.

The engines are intended for working fast passenger trains of 480 tons weight over the difficult Southern Railway main line, and goods and mineral trains of up to 1200 tons; that is to say, something above the heaviest trains that would be required on the system. They carry sufficient fuel for 200 miles. . . .

APPENDIX D

COMPARATIVE TESTS WITH SOUTHERN REGION LOCOMOTIVES

Summary showing comparative performance based on Average results obtained.

EASTLEIGH – WOKING

	Engine No. 31630 'U' Class	Engine No. 36001 'Leader Class'	% Difference Class 'U' = 100%
Boiler pressure (lbs/in.)	187	240	28.3% greater
Steam Chest pressure (lbs/in.)	167	135	19.2% less
Exhaust pressure (lbs/in.)	1.81	7.3/6.0	–
Smokebox vacuum (in. water)	2.34	4.00	71% greater
Inlet Steam Temp. °F	478	546/564	–
Exhaust Steam Temp °F	220	285	29.5%
Smokebox A Steam Temp °F	570	574	0.7%
Smokebox B Steam Temp °F	578	620	7.26%
Trip			–
Coal lbs	1455	2457	68.8%
lbs/mile	29.75	50.17	68.7%
lbs/ton mile (incl engine)	0.0818	0.121	48.0%
lbs/hr (running time)	1125	1830	62.7%
lbs/sq. ft. grate/hr	45	71.8	59.6%
lbs/ D.B.H.P. hr	4.01	6.727	67.6%
Water gall	1245	1850	48.6%
gall/mile	25.44	37.78	48.5%
lbs/hr (running time)	9621	13790	43.3%
lbs/D.B.H.P. hr	34.34	50.66	47.5%
lbs/sq. ft. evap heating surface/hr	6.334	5.777	8.8% less
lbs/ton mile (incl. engine)	0.702	0.912	30.0% greater
Evaporation lbs. water/lb coal	8.554	7.532	12.0% less
Boiler Efficiency %	78.29	71.22	9.0% less
B. Th U's/D.B.H.P. hr	53893	90262	67.5% greater
Overall Efficiency %	4.72	2.82	40.25% less

APPENDIX E

COSTS OF LEADER PROJECT

	No. 36001			Repairs/ Maintenance No. 36001			Locos Nos. 36002–5			Totals		
	£	s.	d.	£	s.	d.	£	s.	d.	£	s.	d.
Materials	14,144	5	11	2064	14	8	61,478	9	0	77,687	9	7
Wages	14,295	14	1	2644	13	2	37,775	6	2	54,715	13	5
Workshop expenses	10,913	17	4	1621	13	10	28,651	7	0	41,186	18	2
Sup'tendance	1429	11	5	96	16	5	3748	16	0	5275	3	10
Totals	40,783	8	9	6427	18	1	131,653	18	2	178,865	5	0

Figures taken from Riddles reports of March and November 1950.

APPENDIX F

Memorandum by Mr. Bulleid 8.3.1950.

'As I was not satisfied that the axle loadings of the Leader sent to Mr. Riddles were correct I weighed No. 1 bogie at Brighton on 24.2.1950 . . .

The engine was weighed with the boiler full of cold water and with 1000 gallons of water in its tanks and 1¼ tons of coal.

. . . It is most desirable the spring chambers in the bogie frames be throughly cleaned out, all rust removed and the interiors painted with a good paint impervious to oil. When attention has been given to these points the engine should be rewheeled and reweighed and the springs readjusted. The engine should then resume its trial running.

The earlier anxieties in connection with the Leader were about the sleeve valves and the brick lining of the firebox.

Although it is unreasonable to expect such a major innovation as a sleeve valve engine to require no development (piston valves took many years to bring them even to their present state), the difficulty experienced through the breakage of the driving wings has been overcome.

The fire brick lining now fitted follows that of oil burning locomotives on which it has given very satisfactory results under more severe conditions. This lining should now give little, if any, trouble.

Other teething troubles may arise and to ascertain what they are, if any, it is essential the locomotive be put back on to the road.

The experience we have had with the engine so far indicates directions in which improvements can be made at a later date, i.e. when proceeding with the building of the remainder of the order.

I am quite satisfied the engine can be made a useful and valuable locomotive and Mr. Granshaw, the Locomotive Manager at Brighton, with the help he is receiving from Mr. Jarvis, the Chief Draughtsman, can be relied upon to see this is done.

I have not referred to the differences in weights between the two sides of the engine. If considered essential this difference can be removed at any time by reducing the water tank on No. 2 bogie on the right hand side by the width of the corridor, by removing the tanks on No. 1 bogie and by providing a new tank on No. 1 bogie ahead of the smokebox. This would improve the weight distribution as between the bogies. I do not consider this work need be done at this stage.

I shall always appreciate deeply having been permitted to follow the development of the Leader engine so far, as it has given me much valuable information for future work.

I would like to add my acknowledgement of the help I have had from everyone concerned and especially the courtesy I have always had from Mr. Riddles.

As I do not think my services are necessary any longer and as I feel I may well be an embarrassment, I shall be oblidged if I can be released from the arrangement made last September. I shall be available for consultation if desired and if I can be of help at any time I shall always be only too pleased to give it.'

(Signed) O.V. Bulleid.

APPENDIX G

Comments on Mr. Bulleid's Memorandum by R.A. Riddles. 24.3.1950.

'The locomotive has been weighed on a number of occasions both at Brighton and Eastleigh.

. . . .It must be stated that the locomotive as at present constructed is not suitable for unrestricted running at the high speeds for which it was designed. The design of the bogies in association with the unusual form of pedestal hornblocks and the particular type of roller bearing axleboxes used is not satisfactory and modifications will be needed if further trial running and dynamometer car tests which will be carried out are sufficiently promising to render this course justifiable.

The sleeve valves with which the six cylinders of this locomotive are fitted represent a major innovation and the need for more development work could reasonably be anticipated. The mechanism driving the valves, as orginally designed, allowed for the usual reciprocating motion combined with a limited amount of rotation of the sleeve valves to distribute the lubricant and equalise wear. Seizure of the sleeve valves has occurred on a number of occasions resulting in broken valves and valve rods . . . .

The mechanisim for imparting the rotational movement to the valves has now been removed, thus eliminating a source of weakness. Insufficinet mileage has since been run to say whether a permanent cure for the failures has been effected.

With the special design of boiler fitted to this locomotive, the inner firebox is not surrounded by water in accordance with normal practice. The firebox sides are built in firebrick supported on steel casing plates. The brick lining has been found to deteriorate very rapidly and in an attempt to overcome the trouble a much thicker lining has recently been fitted. The conditions which the firebox lining of this locomotive are required to withstand are fundamentally different from those existing with oil fired locomotives of conventional design. This lining has not yet been tried in service and it is not possible to say whether it will be free from trouble and have a reasonable life.

The thicker firebrick lining has the effect of reducing the grate area from 43.3 sq.ft. as originally designed, to 25.5 sq.ft., which will reduce the steaming capacity of the locomotive and tend seriously to increase coal consumption at a given rate of working.

. . . . A decision as to whether the remaining four locomotives should be completed must wait the results of further trial runs and dynamometer car tests which will be carried out.

I am not yet satisfied that the expenditure probably necessary to develop the locomotive into a useful and valuable unit will be justified.

A decision on this matter must await results of further trial running and dynamometer car tests. The facts will speak for themsleves in due course.

The weight on the two sides must certainly be equalised before the locomotive can be allowed to run in normal service at the speeds for which it has been designed.'

APPENDIX H

Extracts from R.C. Riddles memorandum to the Railway Executive 20.11.1950.

'In accordance with the terms of R.E. Memo M.2.880 the following further memorandum on the Leader locomotive is submitted.

Since my report dated 24.3.1950 was submitted, further trail runs have been made, including two series of dynamometer car tests to determine the performance of this locomotive in comparison with a conventional locomotive of comparable power characteristics.

. . . It was originally hoped, that adjustment to the axlebox pedestals and slides would improve the weight distribution, but it is now evident that extensive redesign of the locomotive would be necessary in order to obtain a distribution which could be considered satisfactory for running in normal service.

It was therefore necessary in order that further trials might be run, to overcome the unsatisfactory weight distribution temporarily by the addition of 5¼ tons of ballast located on the locomotive in such a way as to produce a more uniform distribution of weight between the left and right sides . . . ..

Renewed running of the locomotive revealed a number of minor defects, which culminated on 29th. June after a total mileage of only 6103, in the crank axle of No. 1 bogie fracturing and breaking in two pieces. Examination of the crank axle of No. 2 bogie revealed a number of small fatigue cracks and this axle would ultimately have failed in similar manner.

. . . The locomotive had to be sent into the Works and new driving wheels and crank axles were fitted on both bogies. With the locomotive as at present built it is very probable that these replaced axles would also fail.

. . . In view of the very high coal and water consumption, it was suspected that steam leakage was occuring and the pistons, sleeve valves and rings, were renewed and examined. Evidence of leakage was apparent and a number of new sleeve rings were fitted and all rings on pistons and valves were renewed . . . .Such a marked deterioration in performance for a locomotive after only approximately 6000 miles is exceptional and the trials have indicated that, with the present design, this rapid deterioration could only be corrected by frequently stopping the locomotive for examination and repairs to the valves and pistons . . . . compared with that of modern main line locomotives of more conventional design where the valves and pistons are normally only examined at intervals of 20–36000 miles . . .

. . . In the course of the trials attention was given to the operating conditions as far as the engine crews are concerned . . . . Men have complained of the high temperature in the firemans cab . . . .the firemans position becomes intolerable if attempts are made to run the engine chimney first, owing to the very hot air which emerges from the corridor when running in this direction. With the present arrangement one of the aims of the locomotive is thus defeated and it would be necessary for turning to take place at the end of each journey.

. . . There are only two alternatives which now present themselves in respect of the future of this class of locomotive. They are;

(a) To make a number of major modifications to the present design with a view to overcoming the difficulties which have been experienced and the difficulties which have been revealed;

or

(b) To scrap the locomotive so far completed and the other four in varying stages of construction.

The former course would involve the following in respect of the matters referred to above;–

(1) The high coal and water consumption is due, to a large extent, to steam leakage past the sleeve valves, pistons and rings. It is also due to the high rate of combustion made necessary by the reduction in grate area, resulting from the thicker firebrick walls which experience shows to be essential.

To correct these deficiencies would, in my opinion, involve a major redesign of the cylinders, eliminating the sleeve valves and replacing them with piston valves . . .

(2) To reduce the total weight of the locomotive by 20 tons, thus bringing it into conformity with the original diagram . . . . would be virtually impossible . . .

(3). . . . At present the boiler is offset from the longitudinal centre line of the locomotive. The weight distribution could be corrected only by placing the boiler on the centre line, which would involve major alterations to the design of the locomotive or by a complete redistribution of the water tanks which also would involve extensive modifications.

In either case it is doubtful whether the present access which exists between the drivers cab and fireman could be retained. This would involve an automatic device in the drivers cab on similar principle to a 'dead-mans' handle on electric stock, (which would be an undesirable though essential complication) or three men would always be required on the locomotive when on the main line.

(4) The present axlebox assembly would require to be completely redesigned to give sufficient freedom to ensure the safety of the locomotive as a vehicle on the track, and to provide the necessary flexibility to eliminate breakage of the crank axle.

It is not possible to say at this stage whether such redesign might not involve the elimination of the chains connecting the coupled axles and their replacement by coupling rods.

(5) It is diffcicult at this stage to suggest anything that could be done to ensure tolerable conditions for the fireman . . .

(6) The defects which are known to exist in the welding of part of the boiler of this locomotive would require to be rectified. Part of the welding of the boiler in the completed locomotive was subjected to X-Ray examination . . . The completed boilers for the other four locomotives, however were not subject to any kind of X-Ray examination and I should not be prepared to allow them to go out into service until this precaution has been duly carried out.

Expenditure amounting to £178,865 has already been incurred. So far it has not been possible, nor will it be possible, to place the locomotive in revenue earning service without further heavy expense. I have not estimated what this further expense might be because, even were it incurred and all the defects eliminated the locomotive, as modified, would offer no advantages compared with one of the conventional well-tried design.

I am compelled therefore to RECOMMEND that the second alternative namely, the completed Locomotive and the other four in various stages of construction, should be scrapped . . . .

(Sgd) R.A. Riddles.

APPENDIX I

The Turf Burner

Following his resignation from the position of C.M.E. of the SR, Bulleid accepted a similar post on the C.I.E. in Ireland.

Almost at once he commenced work on a further novel steam design, officially referred to as 'CC1' and known publicly as the 'Turf Burner'. In many respects the principles of the locomotive followed those previously incorporated in the 'Leader' design and included a machine with total adhesion carried on two powered bogies.

A preliminary start also involved the conversion of an existing steam locomtive to burn peat, for as a country Ireland possessed no natural coal deposits and so the opportunity was taken to take advantage of what local fuel existed.

Following a satisfactory start CC1 took shape at the Inchicore Works. The bogies each incorporated two cylinders this time actuated by piston valves, the final drive was again by chain.

Plans exist for a possible conversion of the engine to oil burning but this was never carried out. Even so there were a number of futuristic principles including a fan assisted draught.

The first outing on the main line was in October 1957 and although several quite successful tests were undertaken the engine never worked a public passenger train although it did operate a number of goods services.

Unfortunately for the engine, Bulleid had retired from Ireland in May 1958 and with him went the impetus for the design. By this time as well there was pressure to convert the system to diesel operation and so after a period in store at Inchicore Works the engine was finally scrapped in 1965.

A full description of the machine is available in *The Turf Burner – Ireland's Last Steam Design* by J.W.P. Rowledge, published by the Irish Railway Record Society.

BIBLIOGRAPHY

Bulleid Last Giant of Steam, Sean Day Lewis, George Allen & Unwin.
Bulleid of the Southern, p. 129, H.A.V. Bulleid, Ian Allen.
Bulleid's Locomotives Brian Haresnape, Ian Allen.
Locomotive Panorama, E.S. Cox, Ian Allen.
Master Builders of Steam, H.A.V. Bulleid, Ian Allen.
The Turf Burner – Ireland's Last Steam Locomotive Design, J.W.P. Rowledge, Irish Railway Record Society.
Chapelon – Genius of French Steam, Col. H.C.B. Rogers, Ian Allen.

Also reports from various issues of:
Engineering
Journal of Locomotive Engineers
Journal of the Stephenson Locomotive Society
Locomotive Railway Carriage and Wagon Review
Mechanical Engineering
Modern Transport
Railway Executive reports on the tests of the 'Leader' Class Locomotive.
Railway Magazine
Railway World
Steam World
The Locomotive
The Railway Gazette
Trains Illustrated

INDEX

LEADER

AND SOUTHERN EXPERIMENTAL STEAM

KEVIN ROBERTSON

CONTENTS

ACKNOWLEDGEMENTS

I am privileged to have been assisted by a number of friends and organizations in the course of preparing this book, a number of which I have only met as a result of the first volume.

With grateful thanks, then, to the following:

Hugh Abbinnett, C. Banks, Don Broughton, R.M. Casserley, Derek Clayton, the late John Click, Barry and Joe Curl, Ken Dobson, Peter Dunk, John Fairman, Ted Forder, John Fry, P.A.L. Millard, the Institution of Mechanical Engineers – especially S.G. Morrison, the National Railway Museum – especially John Edgington and Phil Atkins, British Rail, Reg Randell, Dick Riley, John Scott Morgan, Tony Sedgewick, Ian Shawyer, Pursey Short, A.C. Sterndale, Richard Stumpf, Dennis Tillman, S.C. Townroe, Mike Turner and Les Warnett.

Also to all those who took the trouble to write in following publication of the earlier volume.

Finally, to the staff at Alan Sutton Publishing, for encouragement when it was most needed, and to those at home; perhaps the 'Leader' saga may at last be laid to rest. . . .

INTRODUCTION

The publication of my volume *Leader: Steam's Last Chance*, was the culmination of an idea born many years earlier, which had involved the gathering of as much information as possible on what I had always regarded as a fascinating machine.

From the number of letters received after publication it appeared I was not alone in this quest for the unusual and so – perhaps rashly – I agreed to consider the preparation of a second volume on a similar subject.

As a result of further research I have gone deeper not only into the politics and mechanics of 'Leader' – the latter intended to appease the modelling fraternity – but also into some of the other Southern steam experiments, a number of which are perhaps little known but equally fascinating.

Accordingly the range of cover is broadly from 1921 to 1951, a period when it seemed the Southern, despite having the reputation for being primarily an electric railway, carried out more experimentation with steam than a number of its mainland neighbours. I have not attempted to cover every minor change that affected every engine during the period, but instead categorized these under various headings which I hope will prove interesting and informative to the reader.

From a personal viewpoint, when travelling around the various exhibitions, it is pleasing to watch someone pick up a copy of the original book and start describing it to their friends, intent on impressing the neighbour with their own knowledge. In this way I have heard some wonderful stories about 'Leader', although some should be taken with a pinch of salt – especially that from the man who insisted he had travelled behind 'Leader' from King's Cross to York!

When completing the first book on 'Leader' I was quite certain in my own mind that Bulleid had been wrong in his approach and accordingly misguided. Writing this now though, I am not so sure. Indeed, I have come to a different conclusion: 'Leader' did not fail us, it was us who failed it.

Kevin Robertson
Eastleigh 1990

THE EXPERIMENTAL SPIRIT

Smoke Deflectors

The fitting of smoke deflectors to steam locomotives was an emotive issue to the enthusiast. To a later generation brought up to regard the provision of such equipment as normal the impact was not so great, and indeed on the rare occasions when a locomotive had these embellishments removed, albeit temporarily, the resulting appearance proved strange to the eye.

Smoke deflectors, as the name implies, were provided to trap and deflect forward air currents, thereby directing these upwards, and in so doing carrying the exhaust steam

A Bulleid attempt at steam dispersal, this time intended to allow the exhaust to disperse quickly and so avoid the position of a train being obvious to enemy aircraft. This was the second of the experiments Bulleid had carried out with multiple chimneys: a photograph of the two-chimney machine appears in *Leader: Steam's Last Chance*. In both cases no significant advantage was gained, apart from soot removal from overbridges and tunnels! The additions hardly assisted the graceful lines of No. 783 *Sir Gillemere* and were removed shortly afterwards

B. Curl Collection

and smoke high above the driver's cab and maintaining good visibility – that is if the forward vision from any large tender engine could ever be considered good!

The attention of the locomotive designer to the problem of drifting smoke can be traced back to as early as 1850, when locomotives on the Edinburgh and Glasgow Railway had a semi-circular plate fastened in front of and inside the chimney, projecting upwards a matter of inches. This became known as the 'capuchon', although its use at this time must be suspect, for coke was then in use as a locomotive fuel and accordingly smoke emission was virtually non-existent. Various other designers continued to embellish their engines with this feature although as time passed so the raised lip was reduced, and with it any possible advantage in deflecting air currents. The capuchon thus became fashionable rather than functional. The exception to this was on the Highland Railway, where louvers were cast into the outer casing of the chimney in an attempt to deflect air currents upwards. It was not a successful modification.

Meanwhile, the continued development of the steam engine into a larger and faster machine had exacerbated the problem of drifting smoke. Bigger boilers and shorter chimneys all contributed to the problem, which had not been apparent in the Victorian and Edwardian eras. By the 1920s, however, steam engines were being built almost to the limit of the available loading gauge and in consequence the chimney height could not be much above that of the cab roof. Allied to this, improvements in cylinder and front end design had contributed to the more efficient use of steam, and accordingly when running, much time was spent working with a shorter cut-off and consequent softer blast from the exhaust steam. The exhaust would thus be ejected only a short distance vertically before being caught in the forward movement of air and pushed downwards and sideways, obscuring the cab windows.

Such difficulties were equally noticeable to the occupants of the first and second vehicles of a train, although in this case the only result would be to obscure the view of the passing countryside, an inconvenience rather than a danger.

The problem was first recognized in Germany, where a variety of additional sheets, covers and the like were added at or around the chimney and smokebox in an attempt to effect a cure. As far as Great Britain was concerned, it was the Southern Railway which took the lead, a move eventually resulting in three out of the four main-line companies equipping their locomotives with smoke deflectors. Later still, a number of the BR Standard machines were also dealt with. The exception was the Great Western which with its locomotive designs had utilized a taper boiler and consequently smaller smokebox. This allowed the provision of a taller chimney. The Swindon 'blast' was also greater and accordingly it was never considered necessary to resort to additional outside assistance. But that is not to say that Swindon engines were never affected by drifting smoke, for under certain weather conditions serious problems could occur which, even if smoke deflectors or wing plates, as they were sometimes referred to, had been fitted, would seriously hinder forward vision.

Following a number of complaints from footplate staff and mindful of the risk of a driver missing the indication of a signal, the SR in 1926 fitted 'King Arthur' 4–6–0 No. E450 *Sir Kay* with a pair of small wing plates behind the chimney, extending rearwards a matter of about two feet. Quite what this was intended to achieve is not clear: it is regrettable that any reports of trials with this and the subsequent fittings have failed to survive. Another experiment at this time involved an additional steam blower at the back of the chimney which was turned on when conditions were poor. Although reasonably effective it was wasteful in its excessive consumption of live steam.

It was felt by at least one senior locomotive engineer working on the Southern, J. Clayton, that the geographical location of the former South Western lines was a

Modified with an open cowling atop the chimney, intended to deflect the air flow so that the exhaust is lifted clear, 'King Arthur' class 4–6–0 No. 783 *Sir Gillemere* leaves the GWR locomotive shed at Oxford in June 1927 prior to working a through service back towards the SR. The thoughts of the GWR men on this embellishment are not recorded

H.C. Casserley

contributory factor in terms of drifting smoke and steam. Clayton's view was that the prevailing winds in the country were invariably west to east and so affected the LSWR routes more than those of the LMS and LNER whose main lines ran north to south.

The trials with No. E450 were followed in 1926 and 1927 by four other 'King Arthur' class engines each carrying a different embellishment. The first of these was No. E453 *King Arthur* on which small side plates were affixed parallel to the smokebox. On No. 753 *Melinsande* a curved plate was provided atop and ahead of the front of the smokebox. No. 783 *Sir Gillemere* carried an open box-type structure above the top of the smokebox extending rearwards to the chimney, while on No. 772 *Sir Percivale* contemporary German practice was followed with two large side plates extending down the sides of the smokebox which were secured by straps at the top. Of the four the last mentioned was probably the most obtrusive but also the most efficient, and from the spring of 1928 onwards a number of other engines of the class were similarly modified.

Maunsell, though, was still not satisfied the ultimate had been achieved, a goal obscured by the restrictions created by the German-type deflectors. In particular they left little or no foothold for the driver or others to walk along the side framing when oiling up or for maintenance, while the height of the plates and the necessary smokebox securing straps further obstructed the view from the cab. It was also necessary to take down the plates when drawing out piston valves for examination.

Modifications were then made whereby the plates were set inwards on the running board and cut back so that their forward projection was reduced. However, this considerably reduced their effectiveness and accordingly a compromise was reached

Most effective of all the variants attempted at this time were the side plates fitted to No. 772 *Sir Percivale*. These were in the style of contemporary German practice and although reasonably successful at their desired task were cumbersome in that they needed to be removed at times of valve and piston examination
R. Stumpf Collection

This time with a form of cover protruding forward of the smokebox, No. 753 *Melinsande* approaches Woking in May 1930 at the head of a Southampton–Waterloo via Alton service. With the driver having shut off steam in anticipation of the station stop it is unfortunately not possible to gauge the effectiveness of the modification
H.C. Casserley

Viewed from the opposite side the curved top of the deflector plate is apparent while the necessary mounting strap securing the top to the smokebox is also visible

R.K. Blencowe Collection

which, although not as efficient as the first type, afforded enough smoke clearance without hampering access or maintenance. The modified design of side plates was subsequently fitted to all of the 'King Arthur' class engines and later extended to the majority of other SR steam tender classes likely to work express or semi-fast trains.

While the provision of smoke deflectors continued, in 1931 the SR requested the assistance of the National Physical Laboratory in conducting wind tunnel tests on a 'Schools' class model fitted with a variety of smoke deflectors, including a deflector plate extending back from the smokebox to the cab. The tests identified the areas where difficulties lay and also confirmed the already known fact that height and forward projection of the side plates afforded the best results. Although desirable there were practical limitations to both these features.

An interesting discovery, however, was that the need for smoke deflectors could be all but dispensed with if the shape of the locomotive were modified to reduce forward resistance. In this field the LNER led the way, resulting in the streamlined A4 class.

A side-effect of the fitting of smoke deflectors provided an additional bonus for the crews. It was found that game birds, especially partridge and pheasant, became trapped between the side plates and smokebox where they remained neatly caught, killed but not damaged, and ready for collection at the next stop.

While the problem of drifting smoke had been resolved, at least for the present, it was not to be the end of the story. Some years later the Bulleid Pacific classes would present new problems, with a variety of modifications attempted to effect a cure. Those pertaining to the 'Merchant Navy' class are referred to in A.J. Fry's book on the subject, *Bulleid Power: The 'Merchant Navy' Class* (Alan Sutton, 1990).

Forward vision continued to be a problem and was later blamed for the Milton accident on the Western Region in 1955 as well as the Lewisham disaster two years later. Certainly the 'Leader' design showed it was possible to have the steam engine driver at

The side plates in action: No. 772 working hard on a Victoria to Ramsgate train. The exhaust steam and smoke can be seen to be lifted clear of the boiler to descend beyond the tender

H.C. Casserley

The final variation, and that decided on for general use. No. 768 *Sir Balin* fitted with a compromise design which afforded maximum smoke lifting and minimum disruption to both the driver's view ahead and maintenance. All of the SR's large tender engines were later fitted with similar plates. Beneath the left-hand cylinder, No. 768 can be seen to be fitted with a vacuum pump which was driven off the crosshead. This was a device fitted to a number of SR engines at this time although it was later decided the results achieved, namely the maintenance of vacuum when running without the use of the ejector, were not justified compared with the increased maintenance costs. Accordingly the vacuum pumps were removed. The GWR persisted in the fitting of such devices on its engines up to the demise of steam

History repeating itself at Eastleigh in the late 1950s. The original Bulleid Pacific design had been plagued with problems of drifting smoke from the time of its introduction and accordingly a number of modifications were attempted. These included longer smoke deflectors, curving of the front casing and, as in the case of No. 34049 seen here, no deflector plates

Andrew C. Ingram

the front, ahead of the chimney. In this case visibility was improved, although mechanical efficiency certainly was not.

Trials and Tribulations of the 'Lord Nelson' Class

Introduced in 1926 the 'Lord Nelson' class was, for a while, the pinnacle of locomotive development, as well as holding the accolade of being the most powerful steam design in the country: that is, until the introduction of the GWR 'King' class in 1927.

The sixteen members of the class maintained their position at the head of top link duties on the SR and its successor, BR Southern Region, for over thirty years. Although it has been popular in the past to decry the achievements of the class its record cannot be ignored. Although it lacked perhaps the charisma of the later Bulleid breed, running foremen and crews alike preferred a 'Nelson'. This was because its behaviour was at least predictable compared with the eccentricities of the larger machines.

For the size of the class the engines were the subject of a number of unusual features, modifications and experiments, the lesser-known features being discussed here. The first of these was the provision of a soot blower which was quickly applied to all the members of the class.

The next change affected No. E859 *Lord Hood* which, on Maunsell's directive, was fitted with driving wheels 6 ft 3 in in diameter compared with the standard 6 ft 7 in for

The pioneer 'Lord Nelson', No. 850, depicted in works grey livery at Eastleigh. The engine is in near original condition with small chimney and no smoke deflectors

BR No. 30859 *Lord Hood*, which possessed smaller driving wheels, at 6 ft 3 in diameter, than the rest of the class. On paper this made the engine the most powerful of its type with a nominal tractive effort at 85 per cent boiler pressure of 35,298 lb. The photograph was taken at Eastleigh during the last years of the class, by which time modifications included a large diameter chimney, smoke deflectors and additional side raves to the tender
Andrew C. Ingram

the class. This was the greatest reduction in diameter which could be achieved without major redesign of the frames. The intention was to assess the performance of the engine over the steeply graded Victoria–Dover line, although little difference was found in service. The reduced wheel should in theory have produced a more powerful machine, and indeed the nominal tractive effort (at 85 per cent boiler pressure) was increased from 33,510 lb to 35,298 lb. In service, however, the difference in power was insufficient to warrant further conversions although No. 859 retained its smaller diameter wheels for the remainder of its service. Subsequent members of the class perpetuated the earlier size.

Particularly during the earlier years, driving wheel diameter had been a matter of some debate among engineers, with the generally held theory that locomotive speed was directly proportional to wheel diameter. In addition there was a desire not to exceed certain limits with regard to piston speed and consequently engines were built with 8 ft and even 9 ft driving wheels. It was later realized that such sizes were unnecessary and something in the order of 6–7 ft became the accepted norm for express engines. Indeed, the Bulleid Pacific classes of 1941 totally discounted the larger wheel theory: despite having only 6 ft 2 in driving wheels they proved adept at fast running. Later still the BR Standard 9F class, which possessed a driving wheel size of only 5 ft, was found capable of at least 90 mph, the limiting factor now being the front end steam passages.

As built the 'Lord Nelson' class was fitted with a boiler having a length of 13 ft 9 in allied to a Belpaire firebox. Again, for reasons of improving the performance of the class on the Eastern section, a lengthened boiler was fitted to No. E860. This increased the heating surface by 131 sq ft, consequent upon a increase in length of only 10 in. No improvement in steaming was detected although the longer boiler was carried by a number of engines from the class because of later boiler changes at times of overhaul.

Far more noticeable was the extra-large boiler designed and fitted to No. 857 in January 1937. In this a round-top firebox was provided together with combustion chamber, the latter feature meaning the available heating surface from the tubes was reduced. The external diameter of the boiler itself was also larger, with a corresponding effect upon the smoke deflectors, which had to be modified. Although intended as a prelude to the future design of a large 4–8–0, the new boiler was not always felt to be producing the output expected, possibly due to poor water circulation. Following various technical trials no further development was carried out until 1943 when Bulleid had thermic syphons added to the firebox. This also failed to cure the difficulties encountered and the big boiler was withdrawn two years later in 1945. Syphons were not fitted to any other members of the class. In many respects the scrapping of the large boiler was a pity, for Maunsell had achieved a remarkable success in relation to the weight of the vessel. In this the use of 2 per cent nickel steel plates meant that the only increase in weight was one of 16 cwt in working order, and this from a boiler 14 in longer.

Maunsell, in the design of the class, had attempted to achieve a constant and uniform torque, for which reason the cranks were set at 135° compared with the usual 90°. Externally it was noticeable that the exhaust beats were much more rapid than with a conventional engine, giving the impression that acceleration was improved. Coal consumption, however, was felt to be higher than it might and accordingly, when it was suggested to Maunsell that the constant pull of the 135° cranks might be a significant factor, he readily agreed to alter the setting on one member of the class. No. 865 was modified in December 1933 with 90° cranks and although fuel consumption trials were disappointing the engine was well regarded by its crews and retained the unique feature until withdrawal.

Maunsell's experimental large boiler fitted to No. 857 *Lord Howe*. According to certain sources this was intended to be the design of boiler for a proposed 4–8–0 which was never built. Despite its size the boiler provided less heating surface than the conventional 'Lord Nelson' type, with the difference due to the provision of a combustion chamber. Maunsell is said to have personally preferred the visual appearance of a round-top firebox while, despite its size, the big boiler showed considerable advantage in weight-saving, being built of 2 per cent nickel steel. Note the additional diameter has dictated that the smoke deflectors are stepped outwards

The subject of the chimneys carried by the class also forms an interesting feature, with the first change reported in August 1934 when No. 862 was equipped with a Kylchap double chimney at a reported cost of £458. Again no improvement in fuel consumption was noted, although against this acceleration was improved, as was the ability of the engine to perform well on poorer grades of fuel. A second engine, No. 865, was similarly modified in 1938, although both resorted to a conventional chimney in 1942. Bulleid's appearance on the scene led to further chimney and drafting experiments which included the fitting of Lemaitre multiple blastpipe and stovepipe chimney to No. 863. Externally the appearance may have suffered but the engine was transformed into a star performer. Consequently all members of the class were so fitted although the chimney design was improved with the additional fitment of a wide external lip. Bulleid, it seemed, had at last achieved the proper power output from the class. Indeed the modifications of this time confirmed the generally accepted view that a successor also seemed to obtain the best out of his predecessors' designs. Bulleid, though, felt matters could be improved still further and a number of the class were equipped with 10 in diameter piston valves. This time the change was marginal, and according to S.C. Townroe, No. 863, which was not modified, 'was none the worse without it'.

Fitted with a Kylchap double blastpipe and chimney, No. 862 *Lord Collingwood* was one of two engines so modified, the other engine being No. 865. The Kylchap was later removed by Bulleid and sold to the LNER

Stephenson Locomotive Society

Bulleid's multiple-jet blastpipe and wide diameter chimney as fitted to No. 863 *Lord Rodney*, seen at the rear of Eastleigh running shed. The stovepipe style did little to enhance the graceful design and an exterior lip was later added

R. Stumpf Collection

Last of the modifications was that of windscreen wipers. Minor maybe compared with the obvious changes referred to above but essential if the driver was to maintain the best forward vision. There had been considerable discussion over the provision of such equipment on steam engines for some years and indeed Holcroft successfully applied such a facility to a 'King Arthur' working from Stewarts Lane during 1927. For reasons not apparent the idea was not used elsewhere, while the technical press concluded such equipment could not be successfully applied to a steam engine due to the types of dirt encountered allied to vibration. On the SR such sceptics were proven wrong when in early 1939, No. 852 was fitted with a hydraulic-powered wiper and washer to the driver's side spectacle plate. This was an immediate success and was later extended to the whole class. For reasons not explained, such a device failed to become standard equipment on steam locomotives in later years. Expense was probably the reason, with management seemingly disinclined to improve even by a small degree the lot of the enginemen.

The Marshall Valve Gear

Unique to the SR was the fitting in 1933/4 of N class 2–6–0 No. 1850 with new cylinders and the 'Marshall' design of valve gear. In this, piston valves above the cylinders controlled the admission of steam as before, although the exhaust was operated by a separate valve gear below the cylinders and controlling slide valves. This valve gear was the invention of Mr J.T. Marshall, who had approached the SR on 7 January 1931 with a view to having an engine converted to his patent mechanism. The Southern was quick to accept the proposal and as early as 21 January a start was made on a contract to cover the work. Unfortunately Marshall himself was taken ill shortly afterwards and died some months later; accordingly it was to be some time before the necessary drawings were available for Eastleigh to commence the conversion work.

An N class 2–6–0, No. 1850, was selected and the conversion work carried out at Eastleigh Works in late 1933 and early 1934. The engine emerged from the Works on 3 February 1934 and was used for preliminary tests before being transferred to the running shed for further trial work on 23 February. There now commenced a series of

Works photograph of N class No. 1850, modified with Marshall valve gear in 1933–4. The additional linkage necessary for the exhaust valves is clearly visible. Notice also the second reversing rod running from the cab

tests involving freight turns between Basingstoke and Southampton. A standard N class 2–6–0, No. 1413 was provided to afford a comparison. In addition No. 1850 is known to have successfully worked a van train to Alton and back on 27 February. Initial results were promising and accordingly No. 1850 was booked for a Basingstoke–Waterloo semi-fast working.

The trials so far had confirmed the 'Marshall' valve gear as affording a slight advantage over a conventional engine, although offset against this were difficulties with increased cylinder back pressure and of course the obvious one of increased complexity. But the gear also had a distinct tendency to knock at speeds above 50 mph. Whether this had any bearing on No. 1850's subsequent failure is not known, for on passing Woking en route for Waterloo the right-hand gear disintegrated without warning, and fortunately without further incident. No. 1850 was noted at Brighton shortly afterwards for re-instatement in conventional form. Only a short time was thus spent in its modified form although the reason for this may well have been the sudden death of its inventor, which left the executors of his estate the not inconsiderable task of completing the necessary drawings.

The engine returned to Eastleigh in June 1934 and was surprisingly placed in store until May 1935 before transfer to Exmouth Junction and later Salisbury. Worth mentioning is that an N1 class 2–6–0 ran for some years with a conjugated valve gear driving the inside motion. Difficulties with the mechanics of the equipment and subsequent unequal distribution of steam led to its removal in 1929. On the LNER, though, Gresley persisted with this type of mechanism and his later A4 and V2 classes were so equipped.

No. 1850 inside Eastleigh Works with indicator shelters added, no doubt in anticipation of a trial run. Tests were made from Eastleigh to Southampton, Basingstoke and Alton and were reasonably successful. Following a mechanical failure at Woking at the head of a passenger train, No. 1850 was reconverted to conventional form, having spent less than six months with the Marshall gear

R. Stumpf Collection

The 'Schools' Class

Maunsell's masterpiece, the 4–4–0 'Schools' class introduced from 1930 to 1935, remained basically unaltered for most of their lives. Agreed, various modifications *were* made affecting the bogies, tender roller bearings, crosshead vacuum pumps, speedometers and drifting valves, but still few changes compared for example with the 'Lord Nelson' design. Indeed Bulleid was so impressed with the forty engines of the class that trials with members of the class fitted with Lemaitre chimneys and multiple jet blastpipes failed to prove any worthwhile savings could be accrued.

One member of the class though was altered beyond all recognition, albeit temporarily, and, as might be expected, at the hands of Bulleid. This was No. 935 *Sevenoaks* and which in February 1938 was modified at Eastleigh with streamlined casing, then very much at the height of fashion.

At this time Bulleid was still the 'new chief' on the Southern and no doubt wished to incorporate certain of his former LNER experiences in his new post. Of course, on the LNER streamlining had become almost an art form and accordingly three Eastleigh Works foremen, George Mills, Monty Hatcher and Charlie Biggs, were despatched to King's Cross depot with instructions to study the front of an A4 Pacific. They returned to inform Bulleid that in their opinion the idea was impractical, though this was certainly not the answer that was wanted. Accordingly they were instructed to 'carry on', although how much of this was down to Bulleid and how much may have been at the insistence of Sir John Elliot, in charge of publicity at Waterloo, is uncertain.

Renumbered No. 999, the former No. 935 emerged from Eastleigh with a plywood and canvas casing running from buffer beam to tender and painted green with yellow bands. There was even a 'Sunny South' logo adorning the smokebox. The result was a hideous affair not dissimilar to the Gresley A4 design, but unsuited to the smaller machine.

According to Bradley the locomotive ran one trial to Micheldever complete with plywood casing, though in the opinion of S.C. Townroe this would seem unlikely. Bulleid's, and possible Sir John Elliot's, intention had been to use the engine on the 'Bournemouth Limited' express, but in its plywood form such thoughts were totally impractical. No. '999' hastily re-entered Eastleigh Works where the offending timber was removed, re-emerging as No. 935. It would be a further three years before a streamlined engine would run again on the Southern.

Rail Washing and De-icing Gear

The problem of traction between steel-tyred driving wheels and steel rails had been one to vex the ingenuity of the inventor almost since the advent of the steam engine, one of the most successful methods of overcoming this problem being the use of sand.

Unfortunately the introduction of track circuiting caused a hiccup to the hitherto accepted means used for there was now the risk that a film would build up between the tyre and rail, meaning that the track circuit could no longer be accepted as a guarantee for 'line clear'.

With its intensive service schedules, particularly in the London area, such a problem was of considerable worry to the Southern, and as a means of negating the difficulty three N class 2–6–0s, Nos 1819–21, were equipped in January 1938 with rail washing gear. This was automatic in its function and came into operation behind the driving

Although not strictly in keeping with the theme of the text in dealing with mechanical and associated alterations, I could not resist this view of No. 30903 sporting an early variant in BR numbering. Few locomotives were dealt with in this way: the background livery is clearly still Southern Railway
R. Stumpf Collection

wheels every time the sanding gear was in use. Different sources contradict the success of the experiment, which is believed to have given positive results. It was, however, not extended at this time and the conclusion may therefore be drawn that possibly the Southern had already found out that the rapid frequency of trains was in itself a realistic cure.

In similar vein, L11 class 4–4–0s Nos 158 and 169 were equipped at Eastleigh in January 1941 with de-icing gear for clearing the electric third rail, which involved an amount of extra plumbing from the dome. Such provision on a steam locomotive would itself appear to be slightly fraught, although following local running-in turns both machines were later based at Nine Elms and presumably used in the London area. It is not certain how long they remained so equipped.

Fire-fighting Engines

In 1941 nine D1 class 0–4–2T engines were converted to mobile fire-fighting machines.

At this time the bombing of London was at its height, with the Southern Railway concerned as to the effect of enemy action, should the civilian fire brigade be unable to reach a fire on railway property quickly enough. There were of course trained fire-fighters and -watchers at most depots and stations, while the Home Office sent a number of 'road pumps' to railway premises which consisted of previously stored equipment from the days of the horse-drawn fire engine. The difficulty was still

Plywood and canvas streamlining applied to 'Schools' class No. 935, temporarily renumbered No. 999. It would appear the idea was to use the engine on the 'Bournemouth Limited' service and while Bradley reports a test run being made with the engine in this condition it would appear unlikely. No. 999 was 'defrocked' shortly afterwards and had its original number restored

Side elevation of the mock-up, which upon study reveals the light fabric used. Although intended by Bulleid to resemble the LNER A4 class, the visual impact was far from satisfactory and no further work was done towards streamlining on Southern engines at the time

Another Bulleid modification to the 'Schools' class was the fitting of a multiple-jet blastpipe and wide diameter chimney. As with the 'Lord Nelson' design, the new embellishments did little for the visual impact of the class and a lipped chimney was later substituted

B.W. Anwell

D1 0-4-2T No. 2357, seen here when converted to a fire-fighting machine. In its modified form No. 2357 was originally allocated to Bricklayers Arms depot, although it is not thought it was ever called upon to deal with the results of enemy action. The fire-fighting equipment was later removed and the engine restored to conventional use

R. Stumpf Collection

ensuring a fire engine would be able to deal with a fire, particularly if its route was obstructed by damaged buildings or rolling stock.

Accordingly, at the instigation of a foreman from Brighton Works, the railway approached the firm of Merryweathers and 'borrowed' another horse-drawn pump which was experimentally attached to an engine: details of the locomotive used are not reported. This was an immediate success and accordingly the SR Air Raid Precautions Officer requested that ten engines should be similarly equipped.

Similar fire pumps were obtained from Messrs. Shand Mason & Co. at a cost of £73 each and immediately despatched to Eastleigh. The choice of locomotives to be used was also made and ten D1 locomotives, Nos 2215, 2220, 2239, 2244, 2252, 2253, 2255, 2260, 2357 and 2359 were despatched to the Hampshire works. The conversion work was quickly completed and involved mounting the fire pump on the rear of the bunker in the space formerly occupied by the toolbox. Access was from opening doors at the rear of the bunker. Three lengths of suction pipe ran from the front of the side tanks to the smokebox, which could be used to gather supplies of water. At the same time the condensing gear fitted to the engines was removed and different injectors were provided.

In their new guise each machine could deliver one ton of water (equal to just over 157 gallons) per minute from four jets, although it followed that a prolonged delivery would require outside water supply.

No. 2239 out of use at Hither Green in July 1945. The fire pumps were contained in a large cupboard-type affair located at the rear of the bunker where the fire hoses were attached. The pumps were later removed and No. 2239 returned to its more usual duties

H.C. Casserley

The converted engines were destined for those depots thought likely to be prime enemy targets, with Bradley providing details of the original allocations:

2215 Stewarts Lane
2220 Nine Elms
2239 Hither Green
2244 Feltham
2252 Norwood Junction
2253 New Cross Gate
2255 Brighton
2260 Fratton
2357 Bricklayers Arms

No. 2359 was fitted with pumps but was instead used as a mobile boiler washing plant at New Cross Gate depot.

Each engine was quickly despatched to its new depot upon conversion and it was not long before the first was in use. This was No. 2255 which on 17/18 April 1941 was in steam at Fratton en route to Brighton when an air raid occurred. The engine was quickly manned and successfully used to douse a number of fires caused by incendiary bombs. No 2220 was also reported as in use at Nine Elms on 10/11 May 1941 following enemy action.

A change of depots for some engines followed:

2239 to Maidstone West
2252 to Dover
2357 to Tonbridge

At least one engine, No. 2215, was inspected at Stewarts Lane by the LNER, while a later ARP demonstration found Nos. 2215 and 2255 at Paddock Wood being put through

Languishing in the depths of Nine Elms shed in September 1945, D1 No. 2220 has had its suction hoses removed, although it still retains the pump at the rear of the bunker. This engine, too, later reverted to normal use

H.C. Casserley

Seen from the bunker end, No. 2215 displays its fire pumps at Battersea on 8 September 1945, unusually not contained within the cupboard referred to earlier. The additional equipment was removed from No. 2215 shortly afterwards

H.C. Casserley

their paces extinguishing fires in a number of condemned items of rolling stock. Unfortunately, after an impressive start the jets of water quickly diminished, although it is not known if at the time either machine was connected to an outside supply.

Following the cessation of hostilities, Nos 2220, 2239 and 2260 were quickly condemned, while Nos 2215, 2252, 2253 and 2357 were returned to normal service. No. 2255 was used as a stationary steam supply at Brighton Works and No. 2244 converted for use with the oil fuel workings then being undertaken. The subsequent history of this engine is discussed in the chapter, 'Oil and Other Fuels'.

THE HOLCROFT–ANDERSON CONDENSING TURBINE ENGINE NO. A816

The experiments carried out on No. A816 during the period 1930–5 must rank among some of the most bizarre ever carried out by the Southern Railway affecting the steam engine. Bizarre because here was a device which was proven actually to work in service and so could benefit the company with regard to savings in boiler maintenance. That the experiment was considered to have failed was in reality due to poor design and manufacture of equipment. Twenty years on, with the consequent improvement in technology allied to a will to succeed, the story might have been very different indeed.

Fortunately records pertaining to the events have survived reasonably intact, mainly thanks to the notes taken by Harry Holcroft who was in charge of experiments on the SR up to 1932.

In describing the events of that time it is first necessary to venture back a few years to Glasgow where, in 1925, A.P.H. Anderson was a draughtsman employed in a marine engineering works. Anderson was one of a small group of individuals working independently who felt that there was room for improving the efficiency of the steam engine and in particular there were conditions under which exhaust steam might be compressed and so liquified without an excessive expenditure of power. By doing this heat would be saved by being returned with the feed to the boiler. The theory was simple: by removing some 600 of the 970 BTUs present in each lb of steam, it would be possible to return the exhaust to the boiler using nothing more than an ordinary feed pump, so utilizing only 1–2 per cent of the power output. The exhaust by this time was unable to expand further and accordingly no great effort was required as all the 'kick' had been removed.

Anderson was not in a position to test his theory himself, but with the assistance of another Glasgow engineer, John McCallum, experimental work was started on a stationary steam plant in 1925. Two years later in 1927 their experiments had reached a point whereby it was found that under optimum conditions – these are not detailed further – 70 per cent of the heat content of the exhaust steam could be returned to the boiler. Further compression of the exhaust was uneconomic, as beyond this figure the savings obtained compared unfavourably with the output of power necessary to achieve them.

Interestingly enough the general feeling among the scientific world at the time was that even a 70 per cent saving was impractical if not actually impossible, as witnessed by a quote from an eminent scientist (regretfully no name is given):

> Of course you can compress exhaust steam and return it as feed, but the power expended in so doing would be so great that the net result would not be worth having.

Anderson and McCallum appeared to have proven otherwise although convincing the sceptics would perhaps be an even larger difficulty. They persevered however, and the promise of attractive profits was sufficient to attract investment from within the City. A company, the Steam Heat Conservation Company (SHC), was formed. It was the intention to set up a demonstration of the system within reach of the capital and a favourable response was received from the then privately-owned Surbiton Electricity Generating Station, which was then supplying DC power. Accordingly, a condensing set was connected to the generator at Surbiton and with the aid of a cooling tower produced exactly the savings Anderson had forecast. He himself had intended to apply the system primarily within a marine environment although at an unknown stage it would appear a suggestion was made – by whom, it is not reported – that a railway engine would also be suitable.

The Surbiton installation worked faultlessly and was visited by a number of technical representatives. Among these were those who saw the installation as a fluke although others attempted to identify the installation for what it was.

The SHC had in the meantime contacted Maunsell and at the latter's request Holcroft, as Technical Assistant to Maunsell, visited the Surbiton installation in 1927 and was evidently impressed by what he saw.

The application of the system to a railway engine, however, would require considerable modification compared with a static plant, not least an alternative to the cooling tower arrangement, while the use of a forced fan to draw the fire was also necessary as there would be no blastpipe. Holcroft was shrewd enough to realize that power would be required to operate the fan and accordingly any savings in fuel could be expected to be minimal.

But it was not on the basis of any hoped for fuel economy that Holcroft found the system attractive, for as he reported:

> . . . the system would be of benefit in a locomotive because the steam would work in a closed circuit and the boiler would be mainly fed with hot and virtually distilled water, the amount of make up being small. This would result in the maintenance of a clean boiler and a great reduction in scale formation and concentration of soluble salts. Boiler wash-out periods could be extended, so promoting greater availability. Boiler maintenance and repairs would also be minimized by the favourable conditions.

Indeed boiler maintenance costs had long been one of the prime areas of expense to the engineer and so understandably any method of substantially reducing contamination was eagerly sought after.

A meeting was therefore arranged between Maunsell and representatives of the Steam Heat Conservation Company at which the company attempted to explain the theory behind its equipment. Maunsell, though, was not interested in mere supposition and would only be convinced if a controlled test were carried out at Surbiton. Accordingly this was arranged and with Holcroft present a fuel saving of 29 per cent was achieved compared with conventional atmospheric working. (Although no dates are given it would appear that the meeting took place in late 1928 and the trials in the early part of 1929.)

Arrangements were therefore made for the SR to provide a locomotive to the SHC for experimental purposes and approval for the project was given by the General Manager, Sir Herber Walker. An agreement was then drawn up which detailed that for its part the SHC would provide the necessary specialist equipment while the railway would provide a locomotive, the necessary brackets, pipework and rodding, chimney, uptake and blastpipe, and carry out the actual erection. The financial outlay to the Southern Railway was reported as being the initial cost of the condensing equipment plus a 25 per cent supervision charge. Holcroft was instructed to collaborate with the SHC.

For use in the condensing experiments, the SR selected an N class 2–6–0, No. A816, which is depicted here in conventional style. Following the termination of the trials the engine again reverted to this form
R.K. Blencowe Collection

At this stage detailed drawing work commenced at Eastleigh as well as the selection at an early stage of an N class 2–6–0 because of its low axle loading and adequate room alongside the boiler for fitting the necessary extra equipment.

It was agreed that a steam-driven fan should be provided at the smokebox and that the additional equipment, namely the multibar cooler and compressor, would be duplicated on each side of the engine so as to distribute the additional weight evenly, by an extra 2½ tons per side. The additional equipment increased the total weight of the engine by 5 tons to 66 tons 4 cwt. Each of these sets was capable of dealing with a steaming rate of 12,000 lb per hour, which was deemed to be the normal evaporation rate for an N class locomotive under typical working conditions. The maximum boiler output of the engine was stated to be in the region of 20,000 lb per hour, and the second set of equipment would only then be required under extreme conditions or to act as as a spare.

As a substitute for the cooling tower of the stationary plant, the intention was to redesign the tender to carry a large bank of radiators in conjunction with the necessary steam-driven fans and circulating pumps. Large diameter pipe connections would thus be necessary between the engine and tender to circulate the cooling water. It was quickly recognized, however, that modifications to the tender of the type described would add considerably to the cost and complexity of the apparatus as well as meaning the tender selected would no longer be interchangeable. Despite this, two separate designs for modifications to the tender were prepared although each suffered from complex engineering features.

As an alternative Holcroft suggested a simpler variant. In this, cooling by means of additional fans applied direct to the multibar coolers was envisaged, with the additional element of a fine cold-water spray to carry away heat through evaporation. In this way

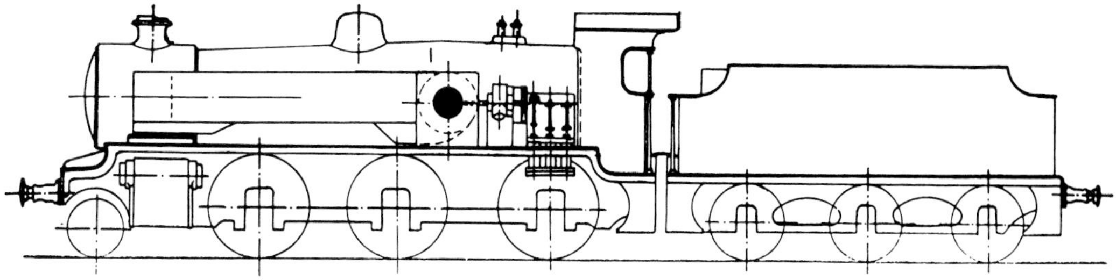

Outline drawing of the modifications as carried out to No. A816. At this stage the original proposal for a bank of cooling fans on the tender had already been discarded

no costly modifications were necessary to the tender. To prove the point, more experimentation was carried out at Surbiton which showed that further fans were not in fact needed to assist the water spray, as in practice all that was required was a water depth of about one foot in the coolers with a direct supply from the tender to make good that lost through evaporation. In what was in effect almost a closed water circuit the tender water thus became used principally for cooling rather than topping up the boiler, with the former supplied from small rotary pumps of the gear type driven off the compressors.

There were in fact two separate water circuits, the first from boiler to cylinders and thence via the cooler and compressor back to the boiler, and the second from cooler to radiators and back through the circulating pump. The coolers were placed one each side of the boiler and the compressors with their small vertical steam engines (donkey engines) either side of the firebox. The fan for the induced draught was driven directly by a rotary steam engine to Anderson's design in which four cylinders arranged radially all drove a single crank on a fixed 25 per cent cut-off. This was fixed to a special smokebox door which drew the gases from the fire and tubes into the smokebox where a reversal of direction occurred before discharge through a chute set at a right angle which led to the base of the chimney. The normal blastpipe was however retained and projected into the chimney chute so that conventional working could be undertaken if required. In practice, conventional working was utilized to get the engine and train moving, with the condensing set brought into use once the engine was on the move. A butterfly valve secured the blastpipe in the closed position which would then bring into use the Anderson system. As might have been expected the provision of a valve in the blastpipe brought about its own difficulties for grit would accumulate above the valve and fall through when it was opened. This in turn worked its way through the system and eventually got onto the seats of the compressor valves, putting them out of action.

Exhaust steam from the base of the blastpipe was conveyed by pipes through the sides of the smokebox to where grease separators were located. A further pipe then led the steam to the multibar coolers where a safety valve set was provided on the header. This was set to discharge at 10 psi.

At the bottom of the rear header of the cooler, the partly condensed steam – much reduced in volume but of course greatly increased in actual density – was conveyed to the compressor and thence via a conventional feed pipe to the clack boxes either side of the dome.

With the necessary drawings prepared, the selection of a suitable member of the N class was made. No. A816 was chosen as it had recently had a general repair and was well run in. Accordingly it was sent from Ashford to Eastleigh where order No. 551 was issued to cover the necessary new works, in the course of which a boiler substitution was also made.

Built at the South Eastern and Chatham Railway's Ashford Works under order No. WO 237/17 of November 1917, No. 816 entered service in December 1922, the last of the class to be completed before the SECR was absorbed into the SR. As built No. 816 sported SECR grey livery but was repainted SR green and renumbered No. A816 in April 1924. The reported cost of construction was given as £5,875 although this was based on 1917 figures.

Between 1922 and 1930 No. A816 had led an undistinguished career and in January 1925 is reported as having been allocated to Battersea together with three other N type engines. Apart from being the first of the class to have its tender fitted with a second tender vacuum cylinder to improve braking, no other major modifications would appear to have been carried out up to 1930.

No. A816 arrived at Eastleigh on 19 June 1930 and entered the works there two days later on 21 June. Conversion work commenced almost immediately and although a number of difficulties were encountered the work was complete and No. A816 ready to leave in its new form by late August 1930.*

The first trials were in September 1930 and undertaken within the Eastleigh Works yard. With steam raised in the conventional manner the smokebox fan for the induced draught was started and immediately blew the contents of the ashpan – cinders and dust – back through the firehole! Due to a misunderstanding the manufacturers of the fan had made the blades the opposite way round to that required and instead of the desired vacuum within the smokebox, pressure was exerted. Despite this an effort was made to operate the engine with the butterfly valve closed (which was operated by mechanical means from the driver's cab), and in this form the engine ran quietly and without any visible exhaust.

A replacement fan was ordered from the suppliers, but this was of indifferent quality and another manufacturer had to be found. Trouble had also been experienced even at this early stage with the steam engine used for driving the fan, and accordingly new pistons were fitted together with improved lubrication.

Difficulties in securing the necessary replacements prevented No. A816 from venturing outside the works and it was not until February 1931 that a light-running trial was attempted on the line between Eastleigh and Romsey, although with the tender handbrake applied at times to represent a load. Unfortunately, during this test the donkey engines ran hot due to failure of the forced lubrication, while the chain drive

* Some discrepancy exists as to the date on which No. A816 entered Eastleigh Works, and for the completion of its conversion and the start of trials. The late D.L. Bradley, an accepted source on SR locomotive matters, gives the entry into the works as 12 July 1930, with the conversion commencing on 16 July 1930. He also states that a number of difficulties were encountered and the engine did not leave the shops until 8 August 1931. From the same source trials are reported to have commenced in September 1931. Bearing in mind the experimental nature of the work this would appear feasible.

The confusion arises, however, in Holcroft's own notes which, besides showing minor variants over the dates of arrival at Eastleigh and entry into the works, are adamant that the work was completed in August 1930 and that trials commenced in September of the same year, a full year earlier than that stated by Bradley. Holcroft is also clear in his workings of the engine for the early part of 1931, which do not correspond with Bradley's account for early 1932, so disproving the theory that a mix-up of years has occurred. Holcroft's notes are themselves assimilated from his own account of his involvement with No. A816 at this time and for this reason it is this source which is quoted in the text.

No. A816 in the course of conversion at Eastleigh in September 1930. As can be seen, at this stage work was almost complete although the tender had still to be painted. The engine retains its circular chimney while it has yet to be discovered that the fan blades have been manufactured the wrong way round!
H.C. Casserley

between the donkey engines and compressors was, according to Holcroft, 'unsatisfactory', and it was decided to substitute gear wheels instead of chains.*

Trials recommenced at the end of April 1931, again light towards Romsey. On this occasion a gear pump broke, as did the valves of the compressors. This it was felt was due to the unrestricted speed at which these components operated and it was decided to fit governors.

Repairs at Eastleigh kept the engine out of use until mid-June 1931 when a test was undertaken to Micheldever, which was 'reasonably satisfactory'. Another run followed on 9 July to Basingstoke and although the condensing equipment on the left-hand side of the engine failed, that on the right gave good results. The engine was reported as working on full regulator at 30–33 per cent cut-off, with at times the tender handbrake screwed on hard. In addition there was the added handicap of the rising 1 in 250 gradient on this stretch of line. Despite all this the fan was able to maintain the desired boiler pressure.

Repairs to the left-hand side then ensued and following a further successful light engine trial to Dunbridge, west of Romsey, it was agreed to attempt a proper load haulage trial. This took place on 31 July 1931 and was from Eastleigh to Basingstoke with a scheduled empty stock train comprising thirty-three assorted vans and coaches

* Holcroft's comments on the unsatisfactory nature of the chain drive used are interesting. Unfortunately no further details of the failure are given and yet they pre-date by over a decade the difficulties that would later be encountered with the Bulleid breed and his chain-driven valve gear on the Pacifics and 'Leader'.

(unfortunately the weights are not given) which was headed by No. E445, a T14 4–6–0. No. A816 was attached to the front of this ensemble and the driver of the T14 instructed only to open his regulator wide enough to ensure lubrication to the cylinders.

The trial was a total failure, and by Winchester, just seven miles from the start, boiler pressure was down to 125 psi on No. A816 accompanied by a large loss of water. Accordingly the test was terminated and No. A816 removed. The van train continued north behind the T14.

Tantalizingly the reasons for the failure are not given and instead an entry appears that the SHC had decided to substitute for the compressors ones of simpler design. These were fitted by the end of August 1931. A further trial to Micheldever was then undertaken and although this was an improvement there was now trouble with the draughting fan. This had been designed to run at a constant 1,000 rpm and was fitted to run with a reducing valve set at 160 psi; accordingly it would operate at a constant speed even if boiler pressure fell by as much as 40 psi from the normal maximum of 200 psi. It was felt an increase in engine performance could be achieved by increasing the fan speed to 1,500 rpm and this was achieved by the simple expedient of removal of the reducing valve. The inevitable occurred and stress failures were found in parts not intended to run at such a high rate. In addition the fan's speed was now totally dependent on boiler pressure and with any reduction in power available, the fan speed would decrease, thereby reducing the draught just when it was needed. Efforts were made to reduce the difficulties by increasing the cut-off of the steam engine driving the fan from 25 to 33 per cent cut-off while a 2 to 1 gear set in the form of sun and planet wheels was installed.

The time spent on these alterations meant that the next trial was not scheduled until 11 November 1931, again with a van train north to Basingstoke. As before No. A816 was coupled ahead of the scheduled train engine, another T14, with the load reported as twenty-two vacuum-braked vehicles comprising 142 axles; again no tonnage is given. Prior to the start a fractured oil pipe was discovered on the right-hand donkey pump which accordingly placed this set out of action. It was, however, decided to continue with the test, working on the left compressor only.

Compared with the earlier load trial north, this time the test proceeded well. The twenty mile climb from Eastleigh to Litchfield Summit was completed in forty-five minutes, with the engine working on full regulator and the reverser in Notch 2¼. Holcroft adds:

> In the ordinary way this would have created much noise and clouds of steam, but with the condensing set in action it was all absorbed with the ease with which snow would melt in a furnace! The engine was as silent as an electric locomotive and the only faint noises were due to slight pounding of the rods and a small blow at a piston gland. This had to be experienced to be believed; but for the regulator being wide open and the reverser well over one would have imagined that the second engine was propelling the first.

In addition, the motley collection of stock necessitated the use of the small ejector at intervals in order to preserve the vacuum and accordingly the injector had also to be used to replace water used by the ejector. Even so the fan maintained boiler pressure at 180 to 190 psi while with the addition of the cold feed, a drop to 170 psi occurred only for a short while.

At Basingstoke the results so far prompted those in charge to continue to Woking where the train was scheduled to terminate, with No. A816 then running light to Nine Elms via Virginia Water and Staines.

Seen from the opposite side there is a good view of the pumps and compressers. When moving away from rest the engine would exhaust in the usual way for a short distance in order to clear away air from the system. With the blastpipe closed for condensing there was a back pressure of around 5 psi in the system. Should this pressure exceed 10 psi the relief valves would blow, which indicated either a larger percentage of air in the system or the existence of greasy water carried over from when the engine was cold. Under normal condensing working only one pump and set of coolers was used, this being sufficient for handling about 66 per cent of the engine's full output. The second set was brought into use if the output exceeded this figure. According to a correspondent in the *Railway Observer* the engine appeared to perform best in hot weather, although this is not referred to by Holcroft

H.C. Casserley

While based at Nine Elms No. A816 is reported as having worked from Waterloo to both Basingstoke and Guildford, although it would seem with only mediocre results. An official comment records: 'For reasons not explained the engine failed to reproduce quite such good form and so was returned to Eastleigh pending the next step to be taken.'

The conclusion at this time was that the mechanical difficulties had generally been overcome although the fan-induced draught was still insufficient for full load working.

Despite this the engine was considered reliable enough to operate empty stock trains from Eastleigh to Brockenhurst and Bournemouth Central and these commenced in December 1931. The average times taken for the thirty mile run are reported as forty minutes coupled to a load of some 180 tons.

In this way No. A816 was now running with some reliability, although the results were far from those originally hoped for. Holcroft too, despite his earlier enthusiasm, seems to have recognized the inevitable and stated:

> This performance was all very well as far as it went, but it seemed to me there was little point in working at half power and that it was useless to continue until there had been a solution of the draught question so that the engine could work the same loads as the normal N class engines.

The Bournemouth workings were supplemented by additional light engine trials north from Eastleigh to either Micheldever or Basingstoke although still there was trouble from the draughting fan. Further modifications were then undertaken within the works, these being sufficient to keep the engine out of traffic until 28 March 1932.

A return to stock working occurred on 12 April 1932, on which day No. A816 worked the 12.50 p.m. empty stock train of vans from Eastleigh to Basingstoke and returned light engine. The following day a similar successful run was made. However, on the same working on 14 April the engine was a complete failure and had to be rescued by an Adams 'Jubilee' 0–4–2 sent from Eastleigh to tow it home. From this time No. A816 resided at the rear of the running shed until 11 July 1932 when the works again attempted to improve the firebox draughting fans.

This time the modification was with the installation of a De Lavel-geared turbine in place of the previous rotary steam engine. On test the turbine proved too extravagant in steam consumption.

Another modification at this time was the replacement of the circular chimney by an unsightly square orifice to which pipes from the condenser outlet were attached. In its condensing form No. A816 could hardly have been referred to as a graceful design and with this new embellishment matters were made considerably worse!

The modification was a serious attempt to utilize the vapour issuing from the coolers so as to create blast in the chimney in place of the fan. It would appear that this was at the instigation of the SHC, as in sceptical fashion Holcroft adds, 'As anticipated, it proved to be a complete wash-out.'

Dormant in Eastleigh Works in June 1933, where No. A816 appeared to spend a lot of its time. It is seen here with the ugly square chimney which it carried for a short while and which was an unsuccessful attempt at improving the draughting

H.C. Casserley

Trials were run again on 4 October 1932; vans and empty stock to Basingstoke, with the engine returning to the works the next day. No. A816 was back on Eastleigh shed on 7 October and three days later on 10 October hauled a further vans and empty stock train to Basingstoke returning again to the works. Although not specified as such it would appear these sporadic runs were to test the various modifications as further light engine trials followed on 23 and 26 January 1933. Further modifications involved strengthening of the running plate below the condensers. Matters had now dragged on for over three years, apparently in excess of the original time-scale agreed between the railway and SHC. Accordingly, an extension of time was sought from the railway and this was granted, although without Holcroft who had moved to other work on the SR. Without the impetus of previous years the experimental work began to falter, though trials were to continue for some time to come.

No. A816 retained its square chimney until mid-1933 and was seen in this form for the last time on 3 May 1933 when it ran from Eastleigh to Basingstoke. It then returned to the works to re-appear on 12 October 1933 with a conventional circular chimney restored and minus the additional plumbing, although still with both condensing sets. On that date the engine was taken to the nearby running shed and prepared for a trial to Basingstoke on 16 November and then on 3 and 4 December to Micheldever. Both the latter runs commenced at 2.30 p.m. A further light engine test to an unreported destination occurred on 6 December.

With the engine not working for some weeks between outings an additional difficulty was discovered, with the condensing equipment failing to operate when started. This was found to be due to pin holes having appeared within the water tubes of the coolers and was attributed to the concentration of salts left in the tubes after evaporation had occurred. The residue was highly corrosive.

No outings are reported at all during 1934 and it is believed No. A816 languished during this time in the Eastleigh Works paint shop. The final series of trials commenced from the works on 20 March 1935 and although not fully documented it is known that on 11 April No. A816 was seen heading north, returning to the shed on 24 April. The days in between were probably spent out of use within the works. Finally on 26 April No. A816 worked to Basingstoke in its condensing form for the last time at the head of eight corridor coaches. The engine returned to the shed where it remained out of use until 24 May 1935 and was then taken to the works for conversion back to a conventional member of the N class.

It would seem that the only remaining difficulty was the intermittent action of the draughting fan and although this could no doubt have been overcome all interest appears to have been lost.

Reconversion commenced at Eastleigh on 27 May, with its re-appearance as an ordinary engine on 16 August 1935. Running-in turns then took place beginning on 19 August with the 6.00 a.m. Bevois Park to Salisbury via Eastleigh goods, returning at 5.30 p.m. to Eastleigh. This was Eastleigh duty No. 315. The following day the 10.00 a.m. stopping train Eastleigh to Bournemouth was worked, returning with a similar working at 9.00 p.m. No. 1816, as she was then, and now minus her rectangular tender plate lettered 'SECR 816', was returned to work from Gillingham (Kent) shed. As BR No. 31816 she survived until January 1966.

With the cessation of the SR's experiments the SHC also seemed to lose its direction, compounded by the death of Anderson in 1938, bankrupt and saddened. Despite this similar condensing equipment was later applied to the boilers of a number of colliery engines in the north of England, although their intermittent use precluded any worthwhile savings being made. The final straw came with the winding-up of the company in 1939, their former London offices and records being destroyed in the Blitz.

The question may be asked why the Southern Railway persued the experiments at all? To this Bradley provides a reasonable supposition. Despite the SR being primarily an electric railway, the conversion appealed to Maunsell and the SR Board because wholesale electrification was still some time away and anything that could save coal and maintenance was worthy of further investigation. It is a matter of regret that none of the other main-line railways appeared to take much interest.

There the story might be expected to end, but not so. Some time later Holcroft, in a meeting with Bulleid, informed the new CME of the previous work which perhaps appealed to the charismatic Bulleid.

Bulleid is alleged to have felt that with the advances that had subsequently been made in aerodynamics a second attempt would have a better chance of success. But during the war the time was not yet right, although a provisional drawing was prepared in which a condensing set was attached to a 'Merchant Navy' Pacific. This drawing showed a 'Merchant Navy' engine fitted with the condensing equipment and with a fan and its casing mounted atop the smokebox in place of the normal chimney. The steam supply to the fan would be taken direct from the main steam pipe from the regulator, with the fan speed thus corresponding to the amount of regulator opening. The generally accepted view that the steam engine should be driven with a wide open regulator would in this case be essential. The coolers and other equipment were as before, either side of the boiler and beneath the casing, while the self-driven compressors were located between the frames, one on either side of the trailing coupled axle. Bulleid had also taken care to ease the passage of smokebox gases to the fan compared with the tortuous route on No. A816. Minor changes were also envisaged to the safety valves and steam heating. Indeed, it must be said that for Bulleid the additions were relatively simple and there was no resort to unnecessary complication.

With the cessation of hostilities in 1945 Holcroft was himself no longer in the best of health and retired in August. Bulleid in the meanwhile was involved in his new design for the Light Pacifics as well as having thoughts about what eventually culminated in 'Leader'. Accordingly, no further work appears to have been done towards the 'Merchant Navy' conversion and one is left to speculate on why this should have been the case. Possibly additional weight was the answer; the equipment on No. A816 added 5 tons to the overall weight. Lack of time with nationalization looming was no doubt the reason a Light Pacific was not selected.

Tantalizingly, a drawing was prepared showing a 'Merchant Navy' boiler temporarily fixed to a stationary plant, to which was added the condensing equipment. The implication is that it may have been intended to take a cautious approach and the assumption is that this was not the direct work of Bulleid who was hardly known for his restraint.

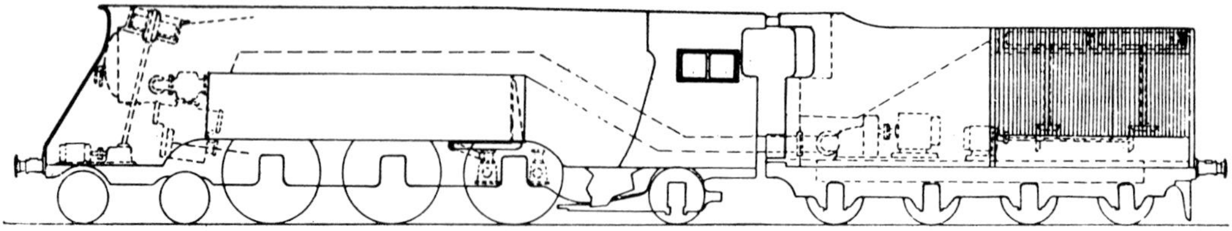

Bulleid's ultimate, a 'Merchant Navy' with condensers and fan-driven assistance to the blast; also, a bank of coolers on a specially enlarged tender. Work on this modification was due to commence following 'Leader'; not surprisingly BR did not proceed with the idea

Bulleid evidently intended to commence work on the experiments following the successful entry into service of the 'Leader' class but, as is well known, nationalization was to prevent any further experimental work on other designs, the new Railway Executive being prepared to concentrate its resources on the less efficient but tried and tested 'conventional' steam design.

By 1950, and living in Ireland, Bulleid continued to develop the theme, this time in an article in the American journal *Mechanical Engineering*. He stated:

> The use of the blast to create draught should give way to fans so that we can control the production of steam accurately. The exhaust steam should not be allowed to escape but should be returned to the boiler. Experimental work already done encourages the thought that these two problems can be solved.*

Holcroft also provides a final drawing of where the ultimate condensing experiment could have led and in this he returned to a bank of cooling fans and radiator grilles carried on a specially built eight-wheeled tender. The idea was to recover all the vapour boiled off in the coolers, with the exhaust steam driving a small turbine which would in turn power an electric generator to provide current to the cooling fans, compressors and draughting fan. In practice it is likely to have caused unnecessary and unreliable complications.

In the Bulleid modified form the condensing system had arguably shown more potential than ever before and it is regrettable that time was to prevent it being allowed to prove itself.

* See Page 101 of *Leader: Steam's Last Chance.*

OIL AND OTHER FUELS

With sufficient natural quantities of coal available within mainland Britain, finding an alternative fuel suitable for the steam engine was for many years a low priority. Events, in the form of rising costs, industrial action and, later, political mismanagement, served to alter the status quo, and accordingly railway engineers were left to seek a replacement for conventional coal fuel.

As far as the Southern Railway and its constituents were concerned, the first to show any inclination towards an alternative fuel was the South Eastern Railway which, as early as 1894, instructed its Locomotive Superintendent, James Stirling, to investigate the feasibility of using oil fuel. This had come about due to the increasing cost of locomotive fuel, which at the time was Aberdare steam coal. Accordingly an approach was made to James Holden on the Great Eastern who had converted twenty-five locomotives to burn both coal and oil fuel. There was also a by-product: the residue left following the production of gas oil was used for carriage lighting. This residue fuel was normally of limited use and Holden thus sought to find a method whereby it might be more gainfully employed.

Investigation revealed that on the GE a 6 in deep coal fire was maintained, onto which gas or creosote oil was sprayed. This somewhat crude arrangement resulted in much dense smoke which took some time to clear. The fuel was obtained from the Stratford gas and oil works of the Great Eastern Railway and it was mentioned that the twenty-five engines used up all the residue available from this means and there was no intention of converting further engines to use this fuel unless cheap imported supplies became available.

As a result the SEC Board took no further action at this stage although the matter was resurrected some years later in 1900 when it was decided to convert two B class 4–4–0s to burn oil/coal using the Holden system. The conversion work was carried out at Ashford, while refuelling was available at Bricklayers Arms and Dover. At the former the risks of oil fuel were evidently seriously considered as two 1,250 gallon tanks were located underground. At Dover supplies were obtained from a rail tank wagon which was kept full, at no cost to the railway, by the Royal Dutch Shell Petroleum Company, presumably in the hope of an increase in orders in the future.

First to be tested was No. 459 which ran a trial from Ashford to Tonbridge on 1 January 1901. Difficulties were soon encountered with freezing of the oil injectors although this was soon overcome by rerouting the pipework. By mid-April 1901 both No. 459 and sister engine No. 454 were passed for general usage, which included Cannon Street to Dover and Hastings services incorporating a number of stops. In July 1902, No. 459 was engulfed in flames within Bricklayers Arms depot, caused by oil dripping from the tanks. The resultant damage was severe enough to prevent the engine working again until December 1902.

In April 1904 Harry Wainwright, the Locomotive Superintendent, was able to report to the Board on the results in service which showed the use of oil to be more costly than

SECR B class 4–4–0 No. 459 being refilled with oil fuel from the underground storage tanks at Bricklayers Arms, probably around 1901. Together with sister engine No. 454 these were the first oil conversions affecting a constituent of the Southern Railway and were designed to burn part oil and part coal. Both engines were reconverted to full coal burning by 1905

coal, with regard to both fuel and maintenance charges. This first saga in the oil-burning story thus came to an end with No. 459 reconverted to coal-firing almost immediately and No. 454 in 1905, following the termination of the oil fuel contract.

Meanwhile the London, Brighton and South Coast Railway had in 1902 announced a programme to convert a number of engines to burn both coal and oil simultaneously. This was considered to be the necessary method of burning heavy oil and was similar to that devised by Holden. It followed that quantities of both coal and oil were carried, with the fireman in charge of the delivery of both fuels, the coal being shovelled through a reduced firehole door. It was referred to as Milburn's system.

Twelve engines were converted at this time, belonging to the B1, B2, B4, D3, E4 and E5 classes, the intention being to gain experience of as wide a range as possible. Fuel was stored at Battersea Yard, with smaller installations at New Cross and Brighton. Oil was supplied by Messrs Samuel & Co. although the railway hoped to locate quantities of oil within the Sussex Downs and accordingly trial borings were commenced.

In service there were complaints about the smell from both passengers and crew, some footplatemen finding it impossible to work under such conditions. Maintenance, too, was increased, with pitting of the fireboxes of certain engines, while lineside and sleeper fires were an ever-present hazard. After consideration of all the factors involved, together with the increased cost of the fuel compared with coal – oil in workable quantities was not located from the trial borings – the contract was terminated in June 1904.

An amusing sequel to the use of oil fuel, but one which could have had serious consequences, concerned the storage tanks at Battersea which, despite the protestations of the Shed Foreman, were quickly given over to the storage of paraffin. This lasted until several small fires occurred, after which the Locomotive Committee relented, the paraffin was quickly drained and the tanks steam-cleaned internally. They were then removed for scrap.*

* A full description of the locomotives involved in this, the first LBSCR oil-burning scheme, may be found on pp. 72–4 in D.L. Bradley's book, *Locomotives of the London, Brighton and South Coast Railway* Part 2, published by the RCTS.

It would appear none of the other railways south of the Thames experimented with oil at this time and it was not until the 1921 fuel crisis that the next moves were made, this time on the South Eastern & Chatham Railway. As before the conversion work first involved the use of oil as an addition to coal, although the amount of coal burnt was minimal and in reality consisted of just a small amount in the back corners of the firebox. The advantage of this was that it allowed for ease of relighting the oil flame as well as preventing the firebox from cooling too much in between times when the oil fuel supply was interrupted. Under these circumstances any coal could be used, even dross. Three engines were selected for conversion, each having different shape fireboxes and using differing burners. The intention was to gain experience as to the most suitable conversion should the coal fuel supply situation deteriorate further. That which was found to be the most suitable would then be produced in quantity. The work was carried out under the auspices of the Chief Mechanical Engineer, R.E.L. Maunsell.

The first of the conversions was in May 1921 and involved an H class 0–4–4T, No. 329 which was fitted with a cylindrical tank across the top of the coal bunker. The choice of No. 329 was a change from the originally selected machine, No. 529 of the same class, but may still be considered surprising bearing in mind the limited space available to carry fuel supplies on a small tank engine. Combustion arrangements for the fuel were based on that previously developed by the Midland Railway at Derby and involved two additional rows of firebricks running longitudinally in the firebox, together with a flash wall built to protect the front tube plate and extending as high as the brick arch. A 'weir'-type burner was placed between the longitudinal rows, which had two narrow slits running along its whole length. The lower of these was for steam, with the oil emerging in the form of a ribbon which dropped onto the steam jets and was immediately pulverized so that it ignited in the flame. The firehole was closed by sliding doors through which steam and oil pipes led via control valves under the care of the fireman.

Tests between Ashford and Maidstone were most satisfactory while further economy was found possible with a modified burner from which the oil issued in a number of smaller streams instead of a ribbon. The additional use of coal allowed the fireman to choose between which fuel was used to maintain boiler pressure. No. 329 was reconverted to coal in August 1922.

On 15 June 1921, an L class 4–4–0, No. 772, was modified using a 'Scarab' oil-burning system. This time the work was a full conversion to oil fuel and involved the removal of the conventional firebars and ashpan and the provision of a shallow 'drip pan' as a replacement. When in operation the firedoor was normally kept closed although a small inspection hole was provided. As before the burner was steam operated and required a 30 psi supply. With the engine out of steam this supply was taken from an adjacent engine standing alongside. Igniting the oil was by the crude yet effective method of inserting a rod with flaming cotton waste at the end through the firehole, although care had to be taken to avoid any blow-back as the gases would immediately seep back on to the footplate and ignite. Duties as an oil burner were at first confined to local workings between Ashford and Hastings, but later a return was made to express duties, in particular the 9.05 a.m. Ashford to Cannon Street service.

The fireman could make adjustments by altering the speed of discharge of the oil and the amount of air that was admitted via the dampers, the latter having no less than forty-eight positions. Although the engine performed reasonably well, trouble was experienced in maintaining boiler pressure as well as with leaking tubes and stays. This was destined to be a common trait with oil-burning engines and was due to the rapid temperature drop once the burner was extinguished. On the plus side there was of course no clinker or smokebox ash to remove at the end of a trip and the only servicing required was the occasional removal of soot from the boiler tubes, which was caused by having too long a flame at the burner. The soot problem could no doubt have been minimized by the fitting of a soot blower, periodically operated within the firebox. As a result of the experience then being gained on the third conversion, the oil-firing equipment was removed from No. 772 on 20 July 1921.

Unfortunately for Maunsell, the short time No. 772 spent as an oil burner had come to the attention of the directors and he was summoned to explain his actions. When questioned Maunsell explained that the firebox was unsuitable for this system of oil firing and therefore it was impossible to maintain a full head of steam when working hard for any length of time. After further questioning he agreed that £140 had been needlessly spent on the conversion.

The third conversion was completed on 18 June 1921, E1 4–4–0 No. 165, which was fitted with a Mexican trough burner. Trials with this were far more satisfactory although it was found that if the oil control valve was opened more than one quarter quantities of smoke were produced. The implication was that combustion was not fully taking place. Following initial work on Ashford–Tonbridge slow trains and then semi-fasts to London, No. 165 was despatched to Battersea for fast workings. Reconversion to coal was not until 11 March 1922.

Unlike on the LBSCR, the SECR fuel used was a gas oil, which, although more expensive than crude or residue oil, had the advantage that it retained viscosity at normal temperature and was easier to handle. Another advantage was that it removed the need to pre-heat the oil either when refuelling or while it was being carried. Both tender engines had a pair of cylindrical oil tanks mounted longitudinally on the tender with flexible connections from the engine.

With coal supplies restored on a regular basis the need for alternative fuel arrangements receded although the burners and other equipment were stored at Ashford should the need arise again in the future.

Meanwhile, at Eastleigh the London and South Western Railway had also been carrying out preliminary work with oil fuel and on 23 April 1921, N15 4–6–0 No. 737 emerged using the Scarab system. It was followed on 18 June by sister engine No. 739. After initial local trials both engines were stationed at Nine Elms and worked to Bournemouth and Salisbury. It was while at the latter depot on 26 July 1921 that No. 739 burst into flames when dripping oil was ignited by embers from a nearby engine. It did not work again in its oil fuel state and was reconverted to coal on 6 August. No. 737 was similarly dealt with on 26 September.

In April 1921 the LSWR converted six engines to burn oil fuel, including N15 class No. 737, at the time unnamed. The use of this type of fuel was short-lived and all had been reconverted to burn coal by the end of the year

On the same day as No. 739 was first converted, 18 June 1921, another engine was dealt with at Eastleigh. This was L12 4–4–0 No. 424, although this time the burner was of the Holden type and no doubt fitted so as to effect a comparison. It was followed shortly afterwards on 25 June 1921 by two more L12s, Nos 415 and 423, although this time again with Scarab burners. Following running-in trials from Eastleigh their duties began to involve work further afield, including Portsmouth–Salisbury and Eastleigh–Bournemouth duties. Later all were transferred to Nine Elms where arrangements were made with the Shell Oil Co. to supply fuel from a temporary 5,000 gallon tank. At Nine Elms work was mainly on Portsmouth services although No. 424 also worked Eastleigh van and Southampton Dock special workings. Reconversion commenced with No. 415 on 14 September 1921 and was followed by No. 423 on 5 October and finally No. 424 on 24 October. No. 424 was reported as the most successful and ran 13,697 miles in its oil-burning form.

Despite the unfortunate experience with No. 739, Eastleigh converted a further engine to oil fuel on 3 September. This was a D15 4–4–0 No. 470 and as it was equipped with a Scarab burner one is left to ponder whether this was the equipment removed from No. 739. The oil fuel was carried in a tank mounted within the tender coal-space although for the purpose a six-wheeled tender was substituted for the eight-wheeled one usually coupled to the engine. Based at the neignbouring Eastleigh running shed, No. 470 commenced with trial runs on local workings before venturing further afield to Bournemouth and Waterloo. Two such return trips were undertaken daily. It remained on this work until reconverted to burn coal on 29 October 1921, at which time the original tender pairing was also restored. Although unconfirmed it is suggested that the engine may also have worked from Nine Elms to both Salisbury and Portsmouth on semi-fast trains. Unfortunately detailed reports of the trials with No. 470 are not recorded, although a lineside observer commented how the engine appeared to emit quantities of dense black smoke.

Eastleigh at this time also converted a single S15 4–6–0 to burn oil. This was No. 515, just twelve days out of the shops when it was recalled for conversion in June 1921. Again the Scarab system was used, at a reported all-in cost of £501.

Following some short trial runs within the works yard, No. 515 re-entered traffic on 30 June and was given a number of local duties. It quickly graduated to Clapham Junction van trains, returning with a Waterloo–Bournemouth working. No. 515 was reconverted to coal on 17 October 1921, having run 7,483 miles on liquid fuel.

In similar fashion to that at Ashford it is alleged that the equipment removed from the engines at Eastleigh was stored pending further use, although the subsequent panic measures of 1926 would tend to cast doubt upon this statement.

The necessity for oil burning was not long in coming again, for in 1926 the General Strike was called and with the miners staying out for some time, there was an urgent need to find an alternative locomotive fuel. Accordingly the past experience of both Ashford and Eastleigh was called upon.

It was on the Western section that fuel supplies first gave rise for concern and, in addition to modifications to the timetable and the curtailment of certain services, arrangements were made to transfer suitably equipped oil-burning engines to Eastleigh. In the event the latter proposition did not occur. H. Holcroft of the Chief Mechanical Engineer's staff was also hurriedly despatched to Derby to arrange for what assistance he could.

With the assistance of equipment from Derby, Eastleigh was expected to be able to equip an engine to burn oil fuel in forty-eight hours at a cost of £110. Dismantling would take a further eight hours. Not surprisingly a number of the engines that had featured in the 1921 scheme were re-equipped.

Accordingly D15 4–4–0, No. E470 was again dealt with at Eastleigh on 10 June 1926 and immediately worked light to Basingstoke to collect all the broken firebricks that shed had for use with the conversions. To carry the oil a rectangular tank 12 ft × 6 ft 8 in × 2 ft 6 in was provided in the tender coal-space which had a capacity of 1,250 gallons. The next day the engine worked a van train from Eastleigh to Clapham Junction with a maximum weight of 298 tons. Holcroft, who was travelling on the engine on this journey, recorded that only twelve shovelfuls of coal were added to supplement the 208.1 gallons of oil used. This related to an average consumption of 23.8 gallons per mile. Following this No. E470 was for a while employed on van trains, notably the 12.00 p.m. Eastleigh–Clapham Junction via Staines service, but later successfully worked the 11.30 a.m. Waterloo–Bournemouth express.

A number of other engines was also converted at the same time including three L12 4–4–0s, No. 424 on 15 June 1926 and No. 420 on 16 June. According to published sources No. 415 was similarly dealt with on 11 February 1926 although this date may well be open to question. All had the Mexican trough delivery system.

For the first month all of the L12s were stationed at Eastleigh and used on van trains and then Eastleigh–Waterloo semi-fast services via Alton. Later they were transferred to Nine Elms for use on Portsmouth services. A difficulty with the oil-burning conversion of the class was in relation to the amount of soot produced, which would eventually lead to furring of the boiler tubes, so preventing proper conduction of heat. An initial remedy carried out by the firemen was to hold a shovelful of dry sand at the firebox door which was then sucked off by the blast, passing through the tubes and scouring them in the process. Meanwhile, Eastleigh was attempting to find a more satisfactory solution, with the cause being recognized as the extreme depth of the L12 firebox compared with other classes. Modifications were accordingly put in hand which involved raising the level of the burner by 9 in so that it was now above the foundation ring. There was a marked improvement in performance following this modification.

Not surprisingly Eastleigh also equipped the two N15 class engines that had been dealt with previously; both had by now been named. No. E739 *King Leodegrance* was converted on 12 June 1921 and No. E737 *King Uther* on 16 June. They were at first employed on main-line van trains between Southampton Docks and Salisbury as well as goods workings to Salisbury and Bournemouth. Following this both were transferred to Nine Elms and used on passenger workings during the day and fitted freight turns at night. The highlight of this particular oil-burning period was on 9 July 1926 when No. E739 headed the 'Atlantic Coast Express' in both directions between Waterloo and Salisbury, including additional stops at Surbiton, Woking, Basingstoke and Andover Junction caused by the general reduction in train services at this time.

Meanwhile, at Ashford H class 4–4–0T No. 329 was again converted to burn oil at a reported cost of £110, together with four engines of the 4–4–0 E1 class as follows:

Number	*Date converted to oil fuel*
A19	12 June 1926
A163	12 June 1926
A165	10 June 1926
A179	9 June 1926

Following initial trials all the tender engines were stationed at Battersea and worked three round trips between Victoria and Dover Marine each twenty-four hours. Such of

Shortage of coal during the 1926 General Strike led to the conversion of a number of engines to burn oil in June 1926 including four E1 class 4–4–0s. No. A163 was dealt with at Ashford and later worked between Victoria and Dover, covering in excess of 15,000 miles before reverting to coal in December of the same year

course was the advantage with oil fuel, for apart from refuelling and general lubrication no time was needed for fire cleaning or ash disposal. Unfortunately, though, there were also disadvantages for it was reported that the smell of the oil proved to be a most effective laxative! The H class tank No. 329 was employed on regular passenger workings from Ashford to Tonbridge, Hastings and Maidstone East.

Around the same time there was discussion over the conversion of the whole K class of 2–6–4Ts to burn oil, although with the strike crumbling the matter was not proceeded with. Accordingly reconversion to coal once again occurred:

Number	*Date reconverted to coal*	*Miles run (if known)*
A19	22 December 1926	18,611
A163	22 December 1926	15,497
A165	18 November 1926	19,203
A179	30 November 1926	13,843
329	22 December 1926	
E470	29 November 1926	
415	4 December 1926	
420	17 December 1926	
424	14 December 1926	
E737	22 December 1926	
E739	17 December 1926	

A particularly interesting experiment was that involving U class Mogul No. A629 which, during the period 1929–32, was converted to burn pulverized fuel. Regrettably the origins of the experiment are not reported although it is known that the necessary equipment was supplied by a German company.

The theory of burning pulverized fuel had been known about for some time and involved the crushing of coal to a fine powder which was then blown into the firebox and burnt. An advantage of the system was that it allowed for the combustion of all grades of coal although set against this were several disadvantages, notably the provision of a crusher either at the refuelling plant or on the locomotive as well as a sealed fuel bunker and additional equipment to transfer the fuel to the firebox. The risk of explosion when dealing with what was in effect a highly combustible powder was another serious consideration.

Maunsell and the SR Board were no doubt aware of all these factors when in 1929 work commenced on the conversion of No. A629 at Ashford. This was completed at the end of the year and on 29 December 1929 the engine left the works. For the purpose of the trials a coal-crushing plant and pulverized fuel storage hopper were erected at Eastbourne locomotive shed which meant that the sphere of working of No. A629 would therefore be restricted.

The conversion affected both the engine and tender, with the latter now containing a large enclosed fuel hopper of 296 cu ft capacity. The base of this hopper was constructed so that the fuel was fed partly by gravity to delivery screws of the Archimedean type. There were three screws, two outer ones for the main feed and a smaller central screw for minor feeding. Unfortunately the size of the fuel bunker and associated equipment restricted the amount of water which could be carried and this was now reduced to 3,300 gallons. A small steam engine mounted on the tender front provided power to the delivery screws and also to a fan located to the rear of the bunker. From the screws the fuel was blown by air supplied by the tender steam engine and a compresser, along

The solitary pulverized fuel engine, No. A629, depicted at Eastbourne in February 1932. Towering above the engine are the crusher and storage bunker for the pulverized fuel, which later burst into flames with amazing consequences. Long periods were spent out of use before reconversion to conventional coal firing in October 1932

H.C. Casserley

A rear view of the pulverized fuel engine which shows the modifications to the tender. The tender fuel bunker was completely enclosed while the fuel was blown forward by an enclosed fan mounted behind the fuel space. In the background is 'Terrier' No. 751 which was used to supply steam to the depot coal crusher and hopper when required

H.C. Casserley

flexible pipes and into the firebox where it entered at the sides. Modifications to the firebox included the removal of the firebars and the substitution of firebricks. The minor, central, feed was used mainly when lighting up.

Initial trials from Ashford commenced in January 1930 after which No. A629 was transferred to Eastbourne for test against No. A627, a conventional member of the U class. An 0–6–0 'Terrier' tank engine, No. 751, was also sent to Eastbourne to act as a stationary steam supply to the fuel crusher and hopper. No. 751 was at this time unique in still retaining its pre-Grouping livery.

For the purpose of the tests both U class engines were equipped with speedometers. A629 proved temperamental although it did on one occasion work the prestige 'Southern Belle' and it is alleged once visited Eastleigh for staff familiarity training. Modifications were carried out at Brighton Works between March and July 1931 aimed at reducing the amount of unburnt and partly consumed fuel which was deposited on the lineside. These were only partly successful and the engine's progress through the Sussex countryside could often be marked by a succession of lineside fires and the ensuing sound of fire engines! Accordingly the mileage run by No. A629 even at this stage was low and long periods were spent stored out of use.

Despite the dangers of this type of fuel as recounted earlier, no difficulties were at first encountered with the bunker at Eastbourne depot. This changed dramatically on an unreported date when a member of the Eastbourne shed staff noticed the bunker showing signs of being likely to erupt and it was wisely decided to empty as much as possible into a number of wagons. After this had been carried out the covers were opened and the blowers turned on to dislodge any remaining pockets of dust. Unfortunately the remaining contents immediately ignited with a tremendous roar and quicky covered a wide area with dense black smoke, no doubt to the chagrin of hoteliers, holidaymakers and the solicitors of the Southern Railway who were kept busy for some time afterwards dealing with claims for compensation.

No. A629 was transferred to Ashford shortly afterwards although it is unlikely much else in the form of trial or train working was undertaken. Maunsell, on being informed of the Eastbourne explosion, immediately cancelled any further work. Re-entry into Ashford Works was in 1932 and No. A629 emerged in conventional form in October 1932, having run only 3,497 miles since December 1929. As with the previous oil-fired experience, the various components remained at the works for a further ten years before being scrapped.

The SR had already realized that any savings achieved in fuel costs by being able to use inferior fuel were more than outweighed by the cost of producing the pulverized fuel and in compensating farmers for crops destroyed in lineside fires. The dangers inherent in the handling and storage of this potentially dangerous fuel were also no doubt considered. Not surprisingly the German manufacturers took a slightly different viewpoint, commenting that the shape of the firebox on the U class was unsuitable and that because of this a greater degree of pulverization was required. This would have added considerably to the cost.

The winter of 1946/7 saw the final involvement of the Southern Railway with oil firing, which was also the most widespread and potentially the most successful. Before going on to detail the locomotives involved it may not be out of place to describe briefly the political situation of the time and the general austerity of the period allied to a country heavily in debt following six years of conflict. Industry was of course working flat out to make good the deficit while the government was also attempting to encourage exports and so gain vital foreign currency. Accordingly, in the export field coal was of prime importance and the best stocks were therefore sent abroad leaving poorer quality fuel available for industry, which included the railways. The lack of available locomotive fuel was particularly felt at some of the smaller depots where it is alleged coal destined for the various merchants was on occasions purloined for locomotive purposes.

Not surprisingly, train services suffered, with criticism levelled at the railway companies although it was hardly their fault. The government then decided to attempt to save even more fuel while recognizing the need for an alternative for the railways. Accordingly, oil firing on a large scale was undertaken, although in the event only two

During its period burning pulverized fuel, photographs of the engine at work are rare so this chance find of No. A629 at the head of the 9.30 a.m. Eastbourne to Victoria was very welcome. It was said the engine's progress would be followed by fire engines, dealing with the results of burning char being deposited at the lineside

of the companies, the GWR* and SR, were to make a serious attempt at converting to this type of fuel, with the Southern leading the way.

Between the four railways, a total of 1,229 engines were to be equipped to burn oil fuel, the quota for the SR being 110. This was broken down into the following classes:

Class	*Original intention to convert*	*Actual number converted*
'West Country'	20	2
N15	16	5
T9	15	13
U	5	2
D15	15	1
L11	10	8
N	29	1
'Terrier'	–	1 (not counted in original figure)

Other sources quote the allocations as 15 × L11, and 10 × D15.

The quotas for the other companies were as follows:

	Intention	*Actual conversions*
GWR	184	37
LMS	485†	24
LNER	450	1 (WD 2–8–0)

From a practical viewpoint it was recognized that the value of oil firing was in the conversion of certain specified areas to be operated on this type of fuel alone and on the SR the area selected was principally the West Country. Accordingly, refuelling plants were envisaged at Exmouth Junction – 25,000 gallons – Wadebridge, Plymouth and Barnstaple Junction, although work was never carried out at the latter three. In addition Eastleigh – 40,000 gallons; Fratton – 5,000 gallons; Salisbury, Basingstoke, Bournemouth and Nine Elms were also equipped. The last four sheds were only ever provided with a rail wagon, steps, hand pump and piping and were designated 'top-up' depots.

The type of fuel oil available was also different from that used previously in that now the choice was a heavy fuel – or residue oil. This had an inherent disadvantage in that when cold it was semi-solid and consequently there was the added complication of it needing to be heated before it could be pumped into a tender. Further heating was also required prior to combustion. All these problems, however, were successfully overcome and on 14 December 1946, N15 4–6–0 No. 740 *Merlin* emerged from Eastleigh Works as the first conversion to burn the new type of fuel. It was fitted with a Mexican trough type of burner while the tender carried a fuel tank of welded construction, with access from a new pair of tubular ladders fixed to the rear. The oil tank was of 1,600 gallon capacity in all the oil-burning conversions and secured to the bottom of the tender by bolts.

* The GWR oil-burning story is referred to at some length in *The Great Western Railway Gas Turbines: A Myth Exposed*, by the present author.

† The LMS proposals included conversion of all of the Beyer-Garratt engines and S & D 2–8–0 classes.

Footplate view of No. 740 *Merlin* at Eastleigh, shortly after being converted to burn oil fuel. On the left is Charlie Dear, who was given the task of instructing the crews on oil firing. Notice the change to the firedoor which contains an inspection hole to observe the flames

S.C. Townroe

The tender of No. 740 with additional pipes for oil delivery and steam warming of the oil. The photograph was taken at Eastleigh shortly after the engine and tender had been released from the nearby works

S.C. Townroe

In its new form No. 740 was sent to the neighbouring running shed where fitters and locomotive crews were instructed on the change. Following a period of local working from Eastleigh the engine was sent to a number of other Southern depots intended to deal with oil fuel. Although reasonably successful it was later found necessary to reduce the blastpipe diameter by $\frac{1}{2}$ in to improve draughting, and other engines of the same class were similarly modified prior to entering service. By August 1947 No. 740 was noted working the 4.52 a.m. Eastleigh–Portsmouth and 9.00 a.m. Portsmouth–Winchester services, returning to Eastleigh with empty stock.

Nine other members of the N15 class were also laid aside at Eastleigh for conversion although only five were later dealt with as follows:

	Date converted	*Date restored to coal burning*
740 *Merlin*	14 December 1946	30 October 1948
745 *Tintagel*	4 October 1947	18 December 1948
748 *Vivien*	27 September 1947	20 November 1948
749 *Iseult*	11 October 1947	20 November 1948
752 *Linette*	27 September 1947	2 October 1948

Details of the remaining four engines intended for conversion are not given. It would appear that in all cases the selection of engines for conversion may have been based on those either due for or recently overhauled.

No. 749 *Iseult* at Eastleigh in April 1948, one of four 'King Arthur' class engines converted at this time. On the left-hand running plate to the rear of the smoke deflector can be seen the steam turbine provided for electric power, most of the Southern oil burners of this period being fitted with this device

W. Gilburt

The last two engines of the class dealt with, Nos 745 and 749, emerged fitted with electric headlamps powered by steam generators; the others had this feature added by January 1948. All were based at Eastleigh with duties including the 7.20 a.m. Eastleigh–Waterloo returning on the 11.30 a.m. Waterloo–Bournemouth. In addition they were to be seen on Waterloo–Salisbury fast passenger services and the 5.05 p.m. Bournemouth West–Waterloo and 6.47 p.m. Waterloo–Bournemouth parcels trains. On one occasion an unidentified member of the group was even reported at the head of the through Bournemouth–Birkenhead passenger which it hauled as far as Oxford.

The conversions were understandably popular with the crews, especially the firemen, although the exception was said to be No. 749 on which the tender fuel tank would move forward under heavy braking. By September 1948 most had been laid aside at

Running well near Shawford on 31 July 1948, No. 748 *Vivien* leaves a trail of dense black smoke as it nears the station at the head of an up working. No. 748 had but a few weeks left as an oil burner before being laid aside pending reconversion to coal

W. Gilburt

Eastleigh pending reconversion, the last active example being No. 745 which on 2 October 1948 was noted at Waterloo having arrived at the head of a relief service from Bournemouth. Following reconversion the electric lighting and tubular tender ladders were retained.

The largest number of SR engines from a single class converted at this time were the thirteen T9 4-4-0s, commencing with No. 305 in January 1947. All were dealt with at Eastleigh and fitted with eight-wheeled double-bogie tenders from S11 class engines. The actual burner fitted was either of the Weir or Mexican trough type, which in both cases consisted of a horizontal fitment mounted across the rear of the firebox spraying fuel sideways and forwards.

In oil fuel form the pioneer No. 305 was run in on local workings and was then set to work on the 7.46 a.m. Eastleigh to Bournemouth, returning with the 11.48 a.m. ex-Bournemouth West. This was a lightly loaded train especially strengthened to 300 tons, although the T9 handled it with a noticeable surplus of steam. On 28 June 1947 it was seen piloting coal burning No. 21C150 between Salisbury and Southampton on the through Plymouth–Brighton service. This train split at Southampton with No. 305 taking the Portsmouth portion while the Pacific continued to Brighton. No. 305 is also reported as having worked the heavy Bristol train for part of its route.

Details of the other conversions are as follows:

No.	*Conversion date*	*Electric lighting fitted*
113	20 September 1947	15 November 1947
114	10 September 1947	28 February 1948
115	30 August 1947	23 December 1947
118	30 August 1947	26 February 1948
121	30 August 1947	24 January 1948
280	15 September 1947	1 November 1947
286	12 September 1947	8 December 1947
303	20 September 1947	9 February 1948
305	18 January 1947	28 February 1948
314	13 September 1947	21 November 1947*
713	2 September 1947	25 October 1947
722	15 September 1947	17 January 1948
731	1 September 1947	31 January 1948

Scheduled to be, but not, converted were Nos 732 and 733.

The engines were similarly run in on local workings from Eastleigh with the eventual allocation as eight at Eastleigh and five at Fratton. Most were to be found working local services between Portsmouth and Salisbury via either Southampton or Eastleigh although there were also occasional visits to Alton, Basingstoke, Bournemouth and as far afield as Weymouth.

Commencing with No. 713 on 25 October 1947, electric lighting and generators were provided, with the generator bolted to the left-hand running plate alongside the smokebox. This facility was destined to be little used as by the early autumn of 1948 all had been laid aside due to a lack of oil fuel. The last active member was No. 286, by then

* Originally intended to use a Laidlaw Drew burner but this was fitted to No. 21C136 instead.

Oil-burning T9 No. 731 and an unidentified coal-burning D14 4–4–0 double-head a through GWR service near Swanwick on 17 August 1948. The electric generator and associated pipework show up well in this view, one of the features greatly appreciated by the footplate crews

W. Gilburt

In the bomb-damaged shed at Fratton, BR No. 30115 awaits its next turn of duty. Most of the tender tanks used at this time were of a standard size and shape, and accordingly it was necessary to pair engines with the correct tenders at the time of conversion

H.C. Casserley

Drummond-designed tender No. 231, formerly with T9 No. 148, awaits its fate at Ashford in March 1956, more than five years after withdrawal. Besides the retention of Southern livery, the tender still retains its oil tank, although the reasons for it being at Ashford are a mystery

H.C. Casserley

BR No. 30286, which headed a Portsmouth–Eastleigh local on 7 October 1948. Not all the oil burners were to receive their BR numbering.

Regrettably none were reconverted to burn coal and after rusting away at the rear of Eastleigh steam shed they were withdrawn in 1951. Following dismantling, the frames from No. 722 were stored at Eastleigh and later married to the boiler and other parts from No. 732, the rebuild being identified by the latter number.

By the middle of October 1947, eight members of the 4–4–0 L11 class had been converted to burn oil, with the work carried out at Eastleigh. Electric lighting was again fitted shortly afterwards, with the necessary equipment in the same location as on the T9 class.

No.	*Conversion date*	*Electric lighting fitted*
148	27 September 1947	24 November 1947
154	4 October 1947	4 October 1947
155	11 October 1947	11 October 1947
157	11 October 1947	11 October 1947
170	4 October 1947	3 January 1948
172	30 September 1947	12 March 1948
411	22 August 1947	13 March 1948
437	25 July 1947	10 January 1948

A line of oil burners awaiting their fate in 1950, led by T9 No. 303. None of the thirteen members of the class converted to burn oil were restored to coal firing

R. Stumpf Collection

L11 class 4–4–0 No. 437 outside Eastleigh shed some time between July 1947 and January 1948. The conversions were reported as free steaming and popular with the crews and were used on a variety of local passenger and goods workings

W. Gilburt

In addition Nos 165, 168, 407, 408, 410, 413 and 414 were scheduled for conversion but the work was not carried out. Again eight-wheeled tenders were provided which carried new tubular access ladders at the rear.

Apart from Nos 170 and 172 at Fratton all were based at Eastleigh and worked local passenger and goods turns to Andover, Salisbury, Fawley, Bournemouth amd Alton. Nos 154, 411 and 437 were also to be regularly seen on Bournemouth semi-fast services while in March 1948 No. 157 was in use as the Poole yard shunter. The last in active service was probably No. 411, seen at Brockenhurst on 30 November 1948. All were then laid aside at Eastleigh and would not work again, although some were not officially withdrawn until as late as April 1952. Judging from the long time-scale before this occurred it would appear there may have been some consideration of possible re-instatement for a number of the class.

The electric generators from the L11 class conversions were removed and later used to provide power for radio communication between the driver and shunter on the 'USA' class shunting Southampton docks. The matter of the electric generators from a number of the other engines withdrawn at the time was of some concern to Eastleigh crews who felt they could easily have been fitted to other steam engines at the depot rather than being scrapped.

It is reported that all the engines converted at this time had large white discs painted on the smokebox door and tender sides. This was to indicate to signalmen that the engine did not require lengthy stops for conventional fire cleaning. Few photographs exist to reveal this feature.

Although all the tender engines converted at this time were provided with a tank of

Seen at Platform 1 of Southampton Central station on a Salisbury to Portsmouth Harbour working, L11 No. 437 is at the head of a rake of LSWR stock. The photograph fails to reveal the presence of a white disc painted on the smokebox which is alleged to have indicated to staff that the locomotive was fitted to burn oil fuel
R. Stumpf Collection

Stored awaiting the cutter's torch, No. 157 rusts at Eastleigh. None of the eight oil-burning L11s were reconverted to coal

N.E. Stead

standard capacity, fuel consumption per mile naturally varied between classes and was also dependent upon the work being carried out. Despite this the heavy oil fuel afforded an improved 'miles per gallon' compared with the equivalent coal fuel. Unfortunately, offset against this were increased boiler and firebox maintenance costs, which were due to difficulties with boiler tubes and broken firebox stays, as well as additional costs in keeping the brick arch and firebox wall bricks secure.

These latter items were provided to protect the firebox sides from the intense heat generated by the burning fuel. Ir addition, the advantage of the oil burner in having its fire lit only when necessary meant that additional stresses of expansion and contraction were provided within the firebox area. The relighting of the fire on an oil burner was itself not without incident on occasions and several men suffered singed eyebrows as a result. There was also the case of the crew on a Portsmouth–Southampton–Salisbury working who had extinguished the fire only to find neither had any matches with which to relight it! Not surprisingly each blamed the other and the matter was not solved until an unscheduled stop was made by Northam Junction signal-box to ask for the assistance of the signalman.

As had occurred in both 1921 and 1926 a solitary member of the D15 class was again converted to oil fuel at Eastleigh in September 1947. This time though the choice was No. 463; a steam generator was added in December 1947 for electric lighting in the cab and at the headlamps. No. 463 was based at Eastleigh and primarily used on local services west as far as Weymouth, including the 11.30 a.m. Waterloo–Bournemouth train which was an Eastleigh loco duty. Fitted with a Mexican trough type of burner it was free steaming and hence popular with the crews. Laid aside at Eastleigh in October 1948 the engine was not reconverted and was officially withdrawn in November 1951.

Interestingly most of the engines converted at this time were early LSWR designs, though the reasons for this are not recorded. Indeed, apart from the 'King Arthur' class, Maunsell designs were poorly represented at this time. However, a number of Maunsell design 2–6–0s were intended for conversion, covering members of both the N and

The solitary D15 class 4–4–0 converted to burn oil, No. 463, seen here with a six-wheeled tender. This engine was used on a number of duties including Waterloo to Bournemouth trains

R. Stumpf Collection

U class 2–6–0 No. 1797 at Fratton in oil-burning form, 11 May 1948. The three engines of this class converted were dealt with at Ashford although only on two was the work actually completed

H.C. Casserley

U classes. In the event work was undertaken on three U class engines and only one N class. On one of the former, No. 1629, it was not completed and restoration was made to coal firing. No. 1629 was of course the engine used in the pulverized fuel trials some years before.

The work on the conversions was undertaken at Ashford, the only time the Kent works had been involved with the 1947 conversions:

No.	*Work commenced on conversion*	*To oil-burning service*	*Reconverted to burn coal*	*Miles run*
1625	3 September 1947	19 October 1947	30 November 1948	27,903
1629	12 September 1947	–	26 October 1947	–
1797	4 July 1947	5 October 1947	27 November 1948	33,169

Nos 1626 and 1629 had run with 4,000 gallon tenders although these were replaced by the slightly smaller 3,500 gallon variant which was better suited to take the welded oil tank. Both were fitted with electric lighting at Eastleigh in January 1948.

Following initial teething troubles Nos 1625 and 1797 were employed on local duties around Eastleigh and Fratton. The various experiments and necessary modifications with the burners were carried out at Eastleigh running shed with no technical advice from outside. Both engines later graduated to Exmouth Junction, from where No. 1625 was also reported as running on the GWR main line between Exeter St Davids and Plymouth via Newton Abbot. Such activities though were short-lived, as by the beginning of October 1948 the locomotives were laid aside at Fratton awaiting reconversion to coal fuel. It is believed this work was carried out at Eastleigh. The other U class engines scheduled for conversion were Nos 1613, 1616, 1635, 1637, 1638, 1795 and 1796.

The solitary N class 2–6–0 converted, No. 1831, was also dealt with at Ashford between 3 June and 18 September 1947. Following brief trials in the local area it was

Rear view of No. 1625 at Fratton in September 1948, running with a 4,000 gallon tender. The electric lighting to the rear of the tender shows up well in the photograph

H.C. Casserley

N class 2–6–0 No. 1831 at Platform 3, Eastleigh in 1948. This was the only member of the class converted and was based at Fratton shed

R. Randell Collection

Only two 'West Country' class Pacifics were converted to burn oil, with No. 21C119 being the least successful. In this form the engine ran just 8,220 miles between July 1947 and September 1948 and was generally accepted to be a poor performer

B.W. Anwell

transferred to Fratton where it worked local duties until being laid aside in September 1948, having run 30,034 miles in oil-burning form. No. 1831 was reconverted to coal burning at Ashford between 8 November and 4 December 1948. It is not reported if electric lighting was ever fitted to this machine. Two further engines of the N class, Nos 1830 and 1859, were also in Ashford for a time for conversion but work ceased early on and they re-appeared as coal burners.

The largest engines to be converted to burn oil were two members of the 'West Country' class. The first of these was No. 21C119 at Eastleigh between 16 June and 26 July 1947. Besides the usual modifications, the four vacuum brake cylinders on the tender were resited, a change brought about by the positioning of the liquid fuel tank.

Initially No. 21C119 was based at Eastleigh and employed on local passenger and freight turns, but later graduated to the 6.00 a.m. Southampton–Waterloo passenger and 11.30 a.m. Waterloo–Bournemouth West trains, which were normally the province of the 'King Arthur' class. However, trouble was experienced with erratic steaming which was due to the presence of the firebox thermic syphons and restricted burner efficiency. This led to the production of much black smoke and was the cause of a number of complaints. In an attempt to remedy the situation a second burner, of the Weir type, was added which, although improving matters slightly, was not entirely satisfactory. Following further trials from Eastleigh the engine was transferred to Exmouth Junction for secondary passenger duties, almost as if the former depot was glad to be rid of a lame duck. In its oil-burning form No. 21C119 (later No.34019) ran just 8,220 miles before being reconverted to burn coal in September 1948.

The second 'West Country' to be converted was No. 21C136, later No. 34036, which was dealt with at Brighton between 9 December 1947 and 28 February 1948. Clearly the poor experience with No. 21C119 had been recognized as from the start the engine was fitted with a 'Swirlyflow' burner at a reputed cost of £640. The engine was immediately transferred to Eastleigh for initial trials which showed up a number of problems. Regrettably these are not fully documented although it is known that a complete failure resulted on one occasion. The difficulties, though, were overcome and after a time spent on local goods and passenger workings, No. 21C136 graduated to fitted freight turns and Waterloo express services, as well as similar West of England duties, including the 'ACE'.

A series of load trials were carried out between Eastleigh and Weymouth with a twenty-coach train as well as another trial with eighteen brand-new coaches from Eastleigh to Basingstoke, for which purpose No. s21C136 (the 's' prefix was added by BR prior to the engine being renumbered 34036 in May 1948) piloted S15 4–6–0 No. 30510. The S15 was provided to help in the starting of the train, after which it became part of the load. Despite the handicap of the 1 in 250 climb from Eastleigh northwards, No. s21C136 was noted passing Winchester not only with ease but releasing excess steam from the safety valves as well! Despite knowing that for the present oil-burning was to be abandoned, the trials were deliberately prolonged so as to gain useful experience in case oil fuel should again be needed in the future. Accordingly it was not until November 1949 that the engine was reconverted to coal, at which time 15,044 miles had been run.

Strangest of all the conversions was that carried out to the Lancing works shunter No. 515S, a 'Brighton Terrier'. This took place in August 1946 and was undertaken in order to give experience to various officials in the use of oil burning on railway engines. Accordingly there was a steady stream of visitors to view No. 515S although she was hardly a good representative at the time as considerable trouble was experienced in keeping the burners alight, partly because of problems in maintaining oil flow. Any

No. 701S at Nine Elms, carrying the inscription 'Oil Pump No. 2'. Just visible are the pumps and connections at the rear of the bunker which connect a rail wagon and the locomotive tender tank
H.C. Casserley

information gleaned was primarily negative! The engine was converted back to coal by October 1947.

The type of burner fitted to each engine varied according to the design of the firebox. Apart from on one of the 'West Country' class engines this was of the Weir or Mexican trough type which was fixed to the rear of the firebox. Fuel would then be sprayed forwards and sideways. This method was found to be the most suitable for engines with a long narrow firebox. To suit the larger machines a Laidlaw Drew or Swirlyflow burner was used, placed low down in the centre of the firebox. This operated in similar fashion to a garden sprinkler, the fuel being ejected by means of steam jets under the control of the fireman. Had any other class been converted which also had a square firebox, such as the LBSCR Atlantic type, then the Laidlaw Drew burner would have been the most suitable.

Besides the engines used for oil fuel burning, two former LBSCR D1 class tank engines were modified to act as pre-heaters and pumps at the depots until the permanent fuel supply installations were available. The first of these was No. 2244 which was modified for use at Fratton. Later it moved to Eastleigh and in October 1947 was renumbered in service stock as No. 700S. Another D1, No. 2284, was similarly modified – where the conversion was carried out is not reported – and sent again to Fratton bearing the number 701S before being despatched to Exmouth Junction. It was also lettered 'Oil Pump No. 2'. No. 701S was later transferred to Nine Elms, both Nos 700S and 701S being hauled by another engine as they were moved from depot to depot. A third D1, No. 2361, was due to become No. 702S but the conversion did not take place.

In their converted form Nos 700S and 701S were attached to tank wagons containing oil fuel, with the D1 kept in steam to enable viscosity to be maintained via the former steam-heating pipes. In addition steam was provided to a pump used to transfer oil fuel

D1 No. 700S, formerly No. 2244, at Eastleigh in use as an oil-pumping engine. The machine was itself coal fired and as it was incapable of movement was coaled by hand from another engine that would be drawn up on an adjacent line. The task of maintaining steam was given to a spare fireman
H.C. Casserley

to the engine tender as required. The duties of maintaining the coal fire in the D1s fell to a spare fireman at the depot.

No. 700S was withdrawn in May 1949 although No. 701S survived nominally on stock until December 1951, despite having been derelict at Nine Elms for some time.

Only three of the depots originally intended to cater for oil fuel were provided with the necessary permanent buildings. That at Eastleigh comprised a boiler house and storage tanks at the rear of the depot while at Fratton a similar large installation was erected at the rear of the shed. Exmouth Junction had a number of storage tanks.

By the end of 1947 official figures quote that only ninety-three out of the intended 1,229 engines had been converted to burn oil country-wide. Indeed, it was already recognized by national government that there had been a serious miscalculation as to the fuel costs of the railway conversions, for the treasury had revealed there was insufficient foreign currency available to purchase the necessary oil. In addition pressure was mounting on the government from the miners' union which saw the conversions as a threat to pits and therefore jobs. Not surprisingly, questions were asked in parliament, although the minister would only respond by blaming the situation on the 'relative coal and oil situations'. There is no record of any financial compensation having been paid to the railway companies although by the time this was applicable nationalization had occurred.

The railways were therefore left in the untenable situation of having spent a not inconsiderable sum on both the locomotives and site installations only to find there was no oil available to purchase. In this way the SR and GWR were the hardest hit although both government and the railway companies were quick to cover up any possible grounds for criticism by stating that the oil-burning locomotives had been replaced in

Temporarily without tank wagons, No. 2244 stands near the office and former dormitory block at Eastleigh in June 1947. Prior to being at Eastleigh, No. 2244 performed a similar role at Fratton. It was withdrawn following the end of the oil fuel programme

W. Gilburt

traffic by coal burners previously stored. This in itself was a somewhat surprising statement as locomotive power was at the time at a premium due to the maintenance arrears from wartime, unless it referred to any machines that might have been stored previously due to a shortage of coal.

As regards the locomotives themselves, the end of the oil-burning period also saw the end for a number of machines. Most, though, were not immediately withdrawn, which gives rise to two possible theories: re-instatement as coal burners or store pending re-use with oil should the situation change.

Meanwhile, at Eastleigh and Fratton the redundant storage tanks were purchased and removed by a local engineering firm, Messrs Selwood, while the Exmouth Junction facility was also hastily removed.

As far as the SR was concerned 1949 was destined to be the end of oil burning with steam locomotives, although not on the GWR where, following the gas turbine fiasco, a solitary Pannier tank was fitted to burn the oil left over after No. 18000 had been withdrawn.

OIL FUEL – THE FIREMAN'S VIEWPOINT

Hugh Abbinnett

Ask any fireman who worked on steam engines in the late 1940s and he will tell you steam had an inherent drawback; namely, the raising of the necessary boiler pressure entailed so much excessive manual labour.

Huge boulders of best Welsh or hard black coal first needed loading onto the tender and then had to be broken up into usable fist-sized nuggets before being fed into a roaring furnace, often at speeds of 80 or even 90 mph. Of course being properly prepared was not easy, and there was always the fireman who had to resort to smashing lumps of coal into a usable size while on the move, which then brought about clouds of dust as well as the wrath of his mate – the driver. Not surprisingly, any fireman welcomed the idea of being able to raise steam without having to resort to such manual labour.

Possibly it was partly in answer to a humble fireman's prayer, that in the summer of 1946 work commenced on the building of some large sheds on spare ground at Eastleigh steam depot. Rumour was rife; new fitting shops, test depot, even an oil depot, were suggested. The latter was given credibility with the arrival of some weirdly-shaped, black matt-painted tanks which took up residence just north of the loco canteen. At least it made a change to look out and see these instead of a steam engine.

All, though, was pure conjecture until one evening the Running Foreman, Freddie Springer, crept into the smoke-filled 'spare' cabin and in his gentle and apologetic manner murmured to Driver Harris, 'There's a few ashes in No. 740 over on the pit. Get your mate to throw the fire out and give the smokebox a good clean, she's over the works on Monday for fitting out for oil burning.'

This was it; oil-burning. The wires of the bush telegraph ran hot, exaggeration went over the top; every engine on the Southern was to be fitted to burn oil. No more shovels, no more fires to clean, the job would be a doddle . . . and so it went on.

How quickly the fireman was brought to earth, for on No. 740 Mr Springer's few ashes turned out to be a firebox full up with one ton of green coal which some over-indulgent individual had kindly provided. It was an unenviable task to clear out this rank, smoking black mass. Eventually all was completed and the next day, Saturday, No. 740 was placed outside the shed on No. 14 road ready for the attention of the cleaners.

All hands now knew her destiny: the first oil burner (presumably memories were short from 1926!) and No. 740 had to look her best. Up on the boiler the Chargeman Cleaner, Charlie Ganger, polished her dome while the youngest member of the gang got the roughest job – scraping the wheels and cleaning the rods and motion. The sunshine was reflected in the green gloss of her paintwork which was embellished with a liberal coating of mineral oil. Even the tender shone, sections of 'fielding' caused where the cleaners had overlapped the marks of cloths folded neatly into 4 in squares.

Straight from conversion to burn oil, T9 Nos 113 and 280 await running-in turns from Eastleigh on 20 September 1947. At this stage neither has been fitted with electric generators
H.C. Casserley

Late on Saturday afternoon No. 740, together with two other engines, was first towed out onto the main line before being propelled back into the works yard, there to await the attention of the fitters and welders on Monday morning.

With the departure of No. 740 the rumours worked up to fever pitch although the everyday grind of shovel and coal pick was enough to bring a daydreaming fireman quickly back to earth.

It was not long before No. 740 returned again from the works, with the tender surmounted by a high black tank giving a definite humpbacked appearance. In the cab there was an additional collection of heavy brass controls. These were located just below the sight feed lubricator on the fireman's side of the cab, almost in front of his small wooden seat. Hardly had she been uncoupled from the M7 which had brought her from the works than inquisitive viewers were scrambling over her fitments; anything to gain an insight as to what the operation of this oil-fired locomotive might be. Close examination revealed the brass wheels to be for such things as 'flashing up' and 'priming', with the more knowledgeable conveying this information to others in the cabin. What they didn't know they made up, but it was all well intended because official instruction was often sadly lacking.

Who then was going to teach us to operate this new form of oil-firing? The answer came with one of the running foremen, Charles Dear, a tall, robust and extremely good-natured man of no small intellect who, it was now noted, had been absent from his duty as a foreman for some time. It was almost as if the railway, in an act of typical clandestine secrecy, had spirited Charlie away to gain the know how which he was now to impart to us, the 'oiler' firemen. 'Oiler' was to become the operative slang for all the oil-fired locomotives.

In addition to the engines, change at the depot was also spoken about, with a new bypass siding to avoid the tailback of coal-fired engines waiting to take on fuel and, of course, once again rumour was rife. Large gantries were spoken of with six or seven steam-heated oil outlets while sandboxes would be filled from pressurized sand pipes. Overhead water cranes would also be erected – life would be so easy from now on.

It was not long before we were dragged down to earth again . . . No. 1 shed road was the first road inside the shed and it was here that locomotives were washed out and descaled and where the fitters carried out repairs which could only be tackled with an engine out of steam. Accordingly, around this part of the shed lay the clutter and rubbish associated with repair work: leather washout pipes, descaling rods, smoke tube rods, plug spanners, all necessary to keep an engine at work. One wet March morning a large rail-mounted oil tank with steam-heating valve attached was shunted into the top of No. 1 shed road, blocks placed under the wheels and the handbrake screwed hard on. Again rumour was rife, which nowadays may appear somewhat ill-informed: cheap fuel from the Navy, battleships being scrapped, cleanings from the tanks at Fawley, and all at one ½d. per gallon. So different from our vision of overhead filling points!

Shortly after this a Brighton tank engine was placed by the tank and used to heat and pump the fuel although again not before the know-alls had had their say. According to them this engine was also to be used as a permanent standby in case of a fire on one of the 'oilers', although the vision of this diminutive engine wheezing its way to where it was needed was, to say the least, in the best tradition of Heath Robinson.

Meanwhile, Charlie Dear had not been idle, and with the tank engine secured to the tank wagon by a multitude of pipes and connectors the first sets of men for training on oil firing were selected and instructed to sign on duty at 8.00 a.m. Monday morning.

The crews soon found there was a distinct disadvantage to the use of oil fuel – the smell. Upon arriving for duty No. 740 was seen attached by pipes to the pump and storage tank while the warmed fluid slowly seeped into the tender. The smell hung around in the air, heavy and all-pervading, and similar to that of creosote on a summer evening. The oil was also a filthy fuel – far worse than coal – and a brush past one of the delivery pipes would leave a smear on one's light blue overalls that belied all attempts to remove it. A partial solution was found with paraffin, though later an even better cure existed and that was to use the liquid contents of the fire extinguishers fitted on each 'oiler'. Consequently, fire extinguishers first on the engines and then in every other location were quickly drained into bottles to be used as a cleaning agent.

Meanwhile Mr Dear, having satisfied himself that there was sufficient fuel in the tender, instructed the crew to 'flash her up', and with a turn on the atomizer valve it was possible to observe a black spray start flowing into the firebox. A well-soaked paraffin rag held in the priming tongs was then set alight and the whole burning mass pushed through the firebox door. Now came the sound every 'oiler' man was to get to know and love – 'whoof' – and a quick glance in the firebox revealed it immediately to be a raging inferno as the spray from the atomizer became a burning fountain. Another glance, this time at the chimney, revealed that for the present at least too much oil was being presented into the firebox, as from the chimney rolls of heavy oily black smoke were evident before settling down onto the previously beautifully clean engine. This heavy black smoke was destined to be a long-lasting problem on the 'oilers'; it drifted over stations, staff, passengers and even allotment holders, all of whom complained bitterly. The latter group were particularly vociferous and many an angry remark was heard from a man whose cabbages were now covered in black or who had lost his prize chrysanthemums!

Eventually the effect of reducing the oil-flow at the atomizer worked and the black smoke gave way to a light grey which finally cleared to heat haze. By this time the water in the boiler gauge glass was starting to jump around slightly, a sure sign of steam being raised, and with it the pressure gauge moved slowly off its stop. With a few pounds of steam raised it was possible to use the blower, which allowed a greater draught to be created and consequent rapid production of steam.

No. 740 was now independent of the tank engine and was duly uncoupled, placed in forward gear and the brakes released. Each man was then instructed individually by Mr Dear, which included moving the engine up and down the shed yard. Included in this instruction was the word 'economy', always a regular component of railway vocabulary.

Charlie Dear, in his pep-talk, added phrases like 'flash up here' and 'close down there' for it was quickly found that once No. 740 was hot she could regain full steam pressure at the turn of a wheel, instantaneous steam as never experienced before by students of the shovel.

On the road it was found there were other disadvantages as well as the smell. One of these was that the atomizer nozzles would choke and thus combustion was ruined, while the additional rows of firebricks laid in the firebox had a habit of collapsing. In addition 'flame outs' were not uncommon when, as the name implies, the flame went out but oil was still being delivered. With a previously hot firebox the result was the copious production of black smoke.

Management quickly found a way to ease the lot of the fireman even further and this came with the provision of a delightful steam-driven electric generator, which was almost like a new toy to the crews. No more cleaning oil lamps, gauge lamps and primitive duck lamps, the latter being no more than a few cotton strands sitting in a bath of oil, with light being produced from a flame at the end of the spout. Instead, the simple expedient of the turning of a valve would set the generator humming and with it the various controls would be illuminated by a strong white light where previously one had groped in perpetual twilight. How primitive our colleagues on a conventional coal-fired engine now seemed.

No. 700S in use pumping at Eastleigh on 20 September 1947. The engine being fuelled is No. 121. On the ground is the pebble bin used by the fireman on coal-burning engines who would collect a shovelful of stones to spread over the firegrate and so reduce clinker sticking to the firebars. The man on the ground alongside the cab of the D1 is Charlie Coles, Shed Chargeman

H.C. Casserley

On the road the engines were almost universally loved, mainly due to the reduction in manual labour. Each crew could also tell its own story about the engines, like the one with the T9 which, having only 160 psi boiler pressure, would leak so badly when the flame was extinguished that pressure was lost in a matter of minutes.

Then there was the incident at Eastleigh shed, caused only because of a lack of experience. On this occasion an 'oiler' was slowly making its way down to the water columns although its progress was blocked by a line of coal-burners on their way to the coal hopper. Accordingly the crew of the 'oiler' jumped off, leaving their steed. A little later the queue moved off again although this time with no one to move the next engine and it was left to a young cleaner to assist. Such a move was of course against all the rules but it was already a time-honoured tradition that firemen and even cleaners would assist the shed drivers in moving engines when necessary. In the cab the cleaner soon found the engine was extremely low in steam. A little knowledge though can be dangerous and with the words 'flash her up' ringing in his ears he opened the atomizer. This was a reasonable move as with the firebricks still red hot it was to be expected that she would roar into life. For some reason, though, this failed to occur, while the young lad did not attempt to ignite the liquid which was now running down the inside of the firebox. Eventually it began to drip and form a puddle on the ground under the engine where, as 'luck' would have it, some hot ashes and clinker remained. Ignition occurred but not quite as intended, for the whole of the outside of the engine was immediately enveloped in flames. With fire leaping all around him the young man cowered in the corner of the cab quite expecting to be incinerated at any moment. But help was at hand for the noise of the explosion had already alerted some drivers and firemen nearby who rushed to the scene. One, Driver Spicer, had the foresight to jump on to the engine behind and charge at the blazing machine, so carrying both engines away from the blazing fuel, after which the flames quickly subsided and it was possible to mount the footplate and turn off the oil spray.

Incidents such as this were generally few and far between, partly because the lifetime of the oil burners was so short. No. 740, for example, took another trip to the works to emerge once again as a coal-fired machine ready for another fireman to 'throw out her ashes'. A number of the other classes were never reconverted and lay in the back road at Eastleigh awaiting scrapping. Meanwhile the fireman laboured on with paraffin lamps and wicks and those lovely steam generators just corroded away.

Fond memories, then, of the 'oilers'; yes there were some. Of the driver watching his crew mate gently swinging his legs on his seat and passing the snide comment that the fireman's lot was now easier than his own. But the smell: it stayed in your nose and throat and on your clothes for weeks. Perhaps the coal-fired engine was harder work but it was a lot healthier.

HARTLAND POINT

As a prelude to the 'Leader' design, Bulleid selected another engine as a mobile test bed for the use of sleeve valves of the type he intended to use with 'Leader'. The choice of locomotive was made on the basis of a machine likely to have only a limited period of further use and accordingly the selection fell upon a former LBSCR 'Atlantic'.

While a number of runs with the engine in its rebuilt form were made, full details have regrettably still not come to light and accordingly the number of occasions sleeve valve failure occurred cannot be accurately assessed. Were the difficulties with *Hartland Point* then based on poor design or poor manufacture? And accordingly were the results deliberately suppressed?

The reader is also referred to the original volume *Leader: Steam's Last Chance* for further information on No. 2039 in its sleeve valve form.

No. 2039 *Hartland Point* on the works turntable at Brighton. Bulleid is alleged to have been aware of the shortcomings of the sleeve valve design on this engine and in particular the axial motion imparted. Further time available for experimentation might have allowed these errors to have been eradicated prior to the series of failures later suffered by 'Leader'

J.G. Click/National Railway Musuem

Inside Brighton Works for attention to the right-hand sleeve valve, which shows evidence of heat distortion probably caused by inadequate lubrication. The length of the actual sleeve in comparison with the cylinder is also apparent: notice the front end lugs still attached at the top. Below the cylinder on the workshop floor is the piston

J.G. Click/National Railway Musuem

Front end detail on No. 2039 showing the three connecting hoses, vacuum brake, steam heat and Westinghouse air brake. Again the plethora of oil pipes and connections is obvious, as is the cut-away running plate above the buffer beam. Emptying the smokebox must have been fraught with difficulty
J.G. Click/National Railway Musuem

Alongside the running shed at Brighton, No. 2039 awaits its next move. By storing the locomotive here it was out of the way of other movement and the hard-pressed shed foreman was no doubt glad to forget it when he could!

Don Broughton Collection

A panoramic view of Brighton shed in late July 1947 with No. 2039 visible in the foreground. It is possible to identify a number of other engines, including Nos 2386, 2567, 1325, 2368, 1900 and 2352

Peter Dunk

'LEADER' – THE ULTIMATE EXPERIMENT

Further research allied to the availability of additional information withheld at the time of publication of *Leader: Steam's Last Chance* has provided the opportunity to elaborate further the behind-the-scenes situation of railway politics on the SR in 1948–9.

Bulleid's 'Leader' design finally left Brighton Works on 22 June 1949, driven by six cylinders on two bogies. With no previous experience of this type of engine to draw from it was going to be a difficult task to assess accurately the capabilities of the machine. If ever there had been a case for a national testing station this was surely it. Those plants available at Rugby and Swindon were incapable of dealing with both so many axles and so long a vehicle. Had the length not been a problem then it would have been possible to deal with a single bogie at a time while an external load could have been used to simulate the additional steam supply required to power the second group of axles. As it was, No. 36001 would have to justify itself based only on line and, later, dynamometer car observations.

'Leader' power bogie undergoing steam test at Brighton Works. Steam was supplied at just 8 psi from an adjacent engine via the temporary attachment to the convoluted main steampipe. The bogie was itself on blocks to allow the wheels to rotate. Notice the exhaust position slightly to the rear of the front axle
J.G. Click/National Railway Museum

Within Brighton Works and almost complete – one more flexible hose for steam heating has yet to be added. The engine would appear to be undergoing a steam test, with part of the side adjacent to the cab door of No. 2 end painted black. Alongside is E4 tank No. 32516 with its number painted on the rear of the bunker, a short-lived BR style

J.G. Click/National Railway Museum

But in the form built, even Bulleid it seemed was resigned to recognizing matters were far from ideal. Indeed, in later correspondence between 'OVB' and Reg Curl in 1965, Bulleid commented, 'The oscillating of the sleeves was abandoned because of lack of time to do the experimental work needed; another side-effect of nationalization!' Three years later, writing from Malta, he continued on the same theme: 'No one but those closely concerned could know it was the oscillating of the sleeves which caused so much anxiety and meant so many trials. I often wished I had not listened to the suggestion of — that this oscillation would ensure proper lubrication of the sleeves as it had in the 'Tempest' aeroplanes' sleeve valve engines.'

But would the sleeve valves have behaved better without the oscillating gear? The immediate answer would appear to be in the affirmative, for the oscillating gear was later removed, after which the performance of the valve gear was indeed improved. John Click, too, affords an insight into the thoughts of the time by posing the question: 'Would the sleeve valves on 'Leader' work better than those of *Hartland Point*? They needed to but from an appearance point of view this looked unlikely.'

Even if Bulleid had realized this himself there was in 1948 insufficient time to effect a redesign. From correspondence received by the author it would appear that Bulleid, in using a multi-cylinder design, was attempting to ensure the locomotive could accelerate rapidly and thus, as a steam engine, cause minimal disruption to other services – shades of the 'Decapod' perhaps. In addition the six cylinders available would have provided an even torque. But again, as recounted earlier, the use of six cylinders had not been the ultimate aim, as witness the split-sleeve design dispensed with very early on as

Viewed from the other side and looking at No. 1 end. Here both steampipes and numberplate have been added, although the presence of the cushion above the buffer stock on the right-hand side is a puzzle
National Railway Museum

unworkable. This would have afforded the equivalent of a twelve-cylinder steam engine. Possibly the advantages of a multi-cylinder design were over-played by Bulleid for had he kept to a conventional two cylinders per bogie, the power output characteristics would still have been improved, while allowing for the use of conventional Walschaerts or other valve gear.

Interestingly, Bulleid makes no mention of the difficulties with the dry back firebox, crank axle failures and boiler-welding defects, the latter found by BR. On the subject of excess weight, however, there is but a brief discourse: 'As far as learning the engine weighed 150 tons – something I did not know and wondered how this was found out. The drawing office was not in the habit of making errors in weights.'

Was all of this a rearguard action by Bulleid or the cry of a disappointed man? Probably the latter, for it was surely the course of events that had prevented No. 36001 from being developed as intended and not the genuine intentions of the designer.

Into the daylight for the first time, No. 36001 – as yet without its cast numberplate – is in stark contrast to the E4 tank; No. 2 end is leading

J.G. Click/National Railway Museum

In steam outside Brighton Works on 22 June 1949 and being prepared for its first run. This time the view is of No. 1 end, with the steam emission from the bogie side emanating from the steam turbine-driven oil pump

Don Broughton Collection

Following its return from inspection at Eastleigh, No. 36001 sported a centre BR crest and identification number. In this form the slab side of the engine is presented to the camera outside Brighton Works. The various body panels removable for service can be seen on the side, while it is also just possible to discern the sliding ventilator above the fireman's compartment, which is in the 'open' position. Behind 'Leader' is WD No. 90671, which appears to be fitted with a cast numberplate on the rear of the tender

J.G. Click/National Railway Museum

Fireman Ted Forder in the cab of No. 36001 at Brighton. Ted was the regular man for many of the trials with the engine and recalls it with a certain amount of affection

Courtesy Ted Forder

Handwritten notes in the files of the late J.G. Click, held at the National Railway Museum, suggest Bulleid *had* indeed intended for 'Leader' to burn oil fuel. This, though, is the *only* reference to anything like official information found on the subject. The dry back firebox would probably have been ideal for oil firing. Unfortunately the date of this note is not stated, although it continues by adding that the Traffic Department was against oil firing. Does this then date matters to mid- to late 1948 when the heavy oil supplies promised to the railways were already beginning to dry up? Probably so, and as a result a rapid change had to be made to coal firing. It seems a pity sufficient oil fuel for just the one engine could not have been made available, as was the case on the Western Region with No. 18000 in 1950.

With hindsight, could No. 36001 have been made to work? The answer must be yes – though certainly not in the form the engine emerged and ran during 1949/50, but with oil firing, two cylinders per bogie and a centralized boiler. It would not have been beyond the boundaries of technology to design a remote control for boiler water level and oil fuel control. A giesl ejector and better heat insulation for the crew at No. 1 end would also have been necessary while the slab sides could indeed have made cleaning easy at a mechanical plant. All of this could have been achieved without excessive expense. The ultimate, however, would have been the inclusion of condensing equipment and a smokebox fan similar to that intended for the 'Merchant Navy' class, as outlined by Bulleid in his thoughts to Holcroft following the latter's experiences with No. A816. 'Leader' did indeed lead the way, by showing what it was possible to achieve; it was BR that would be the loser.

No. 36001 in the company of C2X No. 32440 and No. 32038 *Portland Bill*, sister engine to *Hartland Point* although retaining its conventional cylinders and valve gear. The photograph was taken on 17 August 1949 following a successful light engine test run

Don Broughton Collection

Awaiting its next move, No. 36001 stands cold and lifeless at Brighton in the autumn of 1949. At this stage the covers to the front of the cylinders have been removed, as has the sleeve valve oscillating gear. The photograph is of No. 2 end, with the ventilator holes above the corridor visible in the open position
Kelland Collection

Brighton, 3 October 1949, with 'Leader' prior to working a trial to Crowborough. Again No. 2 end is leading while it is just possible to discern an amount of steam emanating from the safety valves
Don Broughton Collection

Platform 6 at Brighton being prepared for a trial run. Load tests would start from the station so as to simulate realistic operating conditions, although as passenger stock was used the station staff took care to see no passengers boarded the train. A number of persons are visible on the platform and although unconfirmed, it is possible the man with the bowler hat is O.V.S. Bulleid

J.G. Click/National Railway Museum

Starting off, No. 36001 darkens the atmosphere around the station with steam and smoke. The man only partly in the cab would appear to be in a somewhat precarious position

J.G. Click/National Railway Museum

Getting away with a number of observers on board. No. 36001 is never known to have run with just a driver and fireman, there always being at least one other person present. Indeed, the total space available in the three cabs allowed a number of men to be carried even if this was not always in comfort
J.G. Click/National Railway Museum

Following a trial to Oxted, No. 36001 has run round its train and awaits the signal to return south to Brighton
J.G. Click/National Railway Museum

On the same occasion but seen from the other side, the engine almost dwarfs the Maunsell-design coaching stock

J.G. Click/National Railway Museum

Forlorn and out of use at Brighton. The solitary windscreen wiper at each end, which cleared the driver's window only, is seen to advantage in the photographs. Note the drive is left hand at No. 1 end and right hand at No. 2 end. Despite the latter the uninterrupted view ahead allowed superb forward vision
J.G. Click/National Railway Museum

A most unusual and useful detail view of the top of the engine showing the sloping end of the coal bunker, TIA tank and water-filler cap. Access to the latter was far from ideal and was through the cab ventilator at No. 2 end
J.G. Click/National Railway Museum

John Click, who was involved with the 'Leader' project under Bulleid. Later he worked on the Turf Burner in Ireland and became Assistant Works Manager at Eastleigh before taking charge of the Rugby Test Plant. Despite subsequently leaving the railway service for teaching he remained an enthusiast of Bulleid's work
J.G. Click/National Railway Museum

A clear view of the front of the cylinders and sleeves following removal of the oscillating gear and dust covers. While removal of the former appeared to assist reliability, lack of the dust covers allowed the ingress of dirt and grit which may well have contributed to further failures

J.G. Click/National Railway Museum

Light engine trial near Lewes, still with the oscillating gear in position but minus covers. The view shows No. 2 end

C.C.B. Herbert

A dramatic view of No. 2 end at Eastleigh on Saturday 19 August 1950. This was just two days before the start of dynamometer car trials and 'a justification to survive'

Pursey C. Short

No. 36001 outside Eastleigh Shed being prepared for duty. The disadvantage of the high water-filler cap is obvious from the photograph, with fireman Sam Talbot emerging from the cab ventilator. Alongside the water column the tell-tale steam emission indicates the oil pump is working correctly. Behind 'Leader' is No. 30784 *Sir Nerovens*

J.G. Click/National Railway Museum

Broadside-on the sheer bulk of the engine is apparent. Also visible is the taupaulin strung across the top of the coal space, the reasons for which are still not clear

J.G. Click/National Railway Museum

In connection with the dynamometer car trials it was necessary to accurately assess the amount of fuel used on each trip. Accordingly, weighed bags of fuel were used although, as can be seen, this involved an amount of physical effort prior to each test run

J.G. Click/National Railway Museum

Almost ready for a test run No. 36001 stands coupled to the former LNER dynamometer car outside Eastleigh shed. The presence of the black smoke would indicate the fireman preparing his fire before leaving. The practice of firing while stationary was normally frowned upon

J.G. Click/National Railway Museum

Within the carriage sidings at Eastleigh and ready for a test to Basingstoke and Woking. The single headcode disc was all that was carried for the test runs which indicated a main-line run over part of the section between Waterloo and Southampton. The 'SPL' carried on the single disc referred to a special
J.G. Click/National Railway Museum

Although it is of indifferent quality I could not resist the inclusion of this photograph, which shows No. 36001 blasting through Winchester at approximately 7.00 p.m. on 21 August 1950. A comment made in *Leader: Steam's Last Chance* referred to the lack of photographs taken of the trials north of Eastleigh, so for rarity value alone this warrants inclusion
P.A.L. Millard

'Leader' in a hitherto totally unphotographed location, Guildford. The engine has arrived following a main-line trial to Woking from Eastleigh and has then worked to Guildford for turning prior to returning to Woking and later Eastleigh. Despite the presence of a cab at each end of the locomotive, the trials crews were only prepared to work No. 36001 for any distance with No. 2 end leading, to avoid the heat which radiated from the smokebox door. Accordingly, recourse was made to the turntable at Guildford shed

J.G. Click/National Railway Museum

The second 'Leader', No. 36002, caught by shafts of sunlight in New Cross Shed during the summer of 1951. By this time its days were numbered, No. 36001 having already been withdrawn and awaiting the the cutter's torch

A.C. Sterndale

Nos 36002 and 36003 together at Bognor, both in unfinished condition. This was the only time two 'Leader' class engines were seen coupled together, Bulleid's dream of the class being worked in multiple under the control of a single driver never being fulfilled

Ken Dobson

SOUTHERN RAILWAY. (1051 K. / 1/42)

Scheduled Mileage ______

($\frac{6}{43}$) *Depot* Brighton   *Class* Leader   *Engine No.* 36001.

Reports received and sent to shops.	Engine arrived.	Work commenced.	Mileage since last Gen. Rep.	Class of Repr.	Boiler No.	Tender No.	Extension of Mileage.	Date to Work.	Repd. at.
20-12-49	16-12-49	16-12-49	None recorded	Weighing	1421		[illegible]	16-12-49	
7-2-50	2-2-50	2-2-50	—do—	"	"		6,427	2-2-50	
25-4-50	17-4-50	17-4-50	—do—	L/Cas	"		6,957	5-6-50	
27-6-50	20-6-50	20-6-50	—do—	L/Cas	"		7,423	29-6-50	
4-7-50	30-6-50	30-6-50	—do—	Non/Class	"		8,091	15-8-50	
4-9-50	28-8-50	28-8-50	—do—	Non/Class.			8,309	21-9-50	

Broken up. B.E. 12/5/51.

Ref. No. 3582.

Engine record card for No. 36001. No similar record was issued for the other engines in the class

National Railway Museum

'LEADER' – THE MECHANICS

The main body unit of 'Leader' consisted of a full-length 'fish-belly' frame which supported the boiler and its ancillaries together with the fuel bunker and water tanks. All were enclosed within a framed sheet-steel casing forming a central fireman's cab with a driving cab at either end. All three cabs were interconnected by a narrow corridor on the left-hand side, assuming No. 1 end (smokebox) to be at the front. To achieve this within the available loading gauge and having a boiler diameter of 6 ft 4 in, it was necessary to offset the boiler by 6 in to the right-hand side, again viewed towards the front.

The two power bogies were six-wheeled, chain-coupled units, each driven by a three-cylinder, simple expansion sleeve valve engine, and fitted with Bulleid's chain-driven variant of the Walschaerts valve gear. All moving parts were flood lubricated within sheet metal oil baths, including the spring rigging. The cylinders were pressure lubricated by a separate system.

A study of the photographs showing the locomotive in the course of construction reveals the extensive use of welded steel fabrication. Indeed, the whole theme of this was for saving weight allied to strength, the effect being to produce 'monocoque' assemblies where possible, leaving only those parts that might require inspection or periodic replacement easily serviceable. Indeed, with the exception of such components as the BFB wheel centres, tyres, buffer stocks, axlebox housings, superheater header and a number of relatively minor parts, the locomotive was largely fabricated or machined from plate, sheet, tube or bar.

At this period electric welding was taking great strides forward and was a highly successful method of marrying steel together. It was a technique unparalleled in the history of steam locomotive construction, where hitherto heavy and expensive machined castings were assembled with either 'fitted' bolts or rivets.

Of course, a bonus of this was that where prototype or one-off experimental work was involved, any minor changes in design during the course of construction could be adjusted by removal of the affected part by the welder. With 'Leader', various structures involved so many novel features that this facility was used to advantage. Components could also easily be modified where either fouls or errors occurred, as the side-effect of other modifications. Welding was restricted to specially selected men and their work was subjected to X-ray examinations

Main frame structure

The main frames were of welded steel fabrication and consisted of two inward-facing channel-section side members of varying depth braced by four major stretcher assemblies and two end channels. The overall length at the centre line was 64 ft 7 in with a

Main frame assembly of 'Leader' complete with its side members and main cross-bracing. The heavy cross-bracing would later support the weight of the boiler assembly. The narrowing towards the front is apparent and this was duplicated at the rear. That nearest the camera would later form No. 1 end of the engine. Immediately ahead of the front of the main frames is a part assembled bogie frame, with No. 2 bogie at the rear end. Apart from the construction of 'Leader' there are a number of other items of interest in the background, including the steam crane, SR electric locomotive and Pacific casing

J.G. Click/National Railway Museum

Boiler, smokebox and bunker in position. Notice the cross-bracing now fitted to the narrowed front of the main frames which will support the cab floor. The hole in the top of the smokebox is for the chimney opening
J.G. Click/National Railway Museum

nominal overall width of 9 ft. For clearance purposes however, both front and rear ends were set inwards to a minimum width of 8 ft at the frame extremities.

A distinct feature was the deep fish-belly of the actual side members. The maximum belly depth was 2 ft 8 in, the lower edge described by a 52 ft radius located 1 in forward of the longitudinal centre line. This blended into a 16½ in channel depth on either side to extend over the lengths of the bogie support stretchers, after which the lower edge tapered upwards and the upper edge dropped downwards with a 9 in radius to produce a 6 in deep channel at each cab end. Each side member channel was braced by no fewer than twenty-seven vertical gussets.

The front and rear beams were of 6 in deep channel set forward at the centre portion to produce the familiar flattened bow front. The two bogie support stretchers were most complex and are perhaps best described as being made up of two transverse box-section longitudinal stretchers to form, in effect, a two-bar letter 'H', when viewed in plan profile. Each bogie was of course supported by two stretchers, the pair at each end being similar, though differing in certain details.

Dealing with the common parts of both first, the front box section stretchers formed the supports for the four segment-shaped steel body-bearing plates. These were riveted to the underside of each stretcher section. Each bearing plate had a fenced segment-shaped enclosure, into which were flush riveted the pads mentioned above; four in each of the longitudinal stretcher sections and six in each of the transverse sections. Of the last mentioned, four out of the six were somewhat reduced in surface area, this being

The firebox assembly, which was plain sheet stiffened by cross-bracing. The bracings at the rear underside of the boiler were for mounting the boiler on the supporting frame cross-bracing. Notice the thermic syphons also on the underside of the boiler

J.G. Click/National Railway Museum

due to having shaped holes cut through the actual bearing plate and lower box section plates at the centre line to allow for the chimney duct on each bogie to exhaust into its respective box section.

The ends of each of the transverse box sections were profiled and welded into the channel-section side frame members. To allow the exhaust steam in the outer transverse box section of the rear stretcher to pass to the similar section on the front stretcher, a raised, flanged pipe was welded into the right-hand side of each top plate of the outer sections of both stretchers. A 7 in internal bore, steel pipe connected both, being routed along the right-hand side of the locomotive to lie within the lower radius of the casing slope immediately above the right-hand slab water tank.

To reduce condensation this pipe was wound with a thick asbestos lagging tape. The top plate of the outer transverse box section of the front stretcher only differed by having a suitably stiffened rectangular hole to which was stud-mounted the main exhaust pipe and through which the spent steam from both bogie units was exhausted. The front stretcher served an additional function by supporting the front boiler mounting. This involved additional extensions to the top plates of both longitudinal box sections to which were added 'Mintex' insulating plates.

Both stretchers were welded into the main side frame members. There were two remaining major stretchers, again of welded steel construction. These were located between the two bogie support stretchers and served to support the boiler and firebox. Since the firebox mounting pad was $9\frac{5}{8}$ in lower than the main boiler mounting cradle pad, it was not practical to support the firebox on the top of a deep cradle structure. Instead a deep box-section cradle stretcher was located immediately to the rear of the firebox with the lower plate having two forward-facing extensions profiled to form support for the right-angle-shaped 'Mintex' pads. The lower plate was suitably gusseted to the underside to support the extensions. Finally, steel bracings were welded across the frames at both ends to provide support for the wood planking of the driver's cab floors.

Boiler, firebox and ancillaries

The all welded steel boiler of 'Leader' was unique among steam engines although it had certain similarities to the earlier Paget design.

The forward barrel section was of the two-ringed type with the front parallel section rolled to a diameter of 6 ft with the seam butt-welded. The second tapered ring rear section was similarly rolled and welded but was coned to a maximum diameter of 6 ft 4 in at the rear. The taper occurred along the top only. Assembly of the rings differed from standard practice in being butt-welded together. The seams of both rings were positioned on the horizontal centre line but on alternate sides. The front tube plate was of $\frac{3}{4}$ in thickness, flanged inwards and butt welded directly to the front ring. To the outside of the front ring was welded an octagonal flange for attachment of the similarly shaped rear flange of the smokebox.

The firebox tube plate, at $\frac{5}{8}$ in thick, was similarly fitted and butt-welded, with the distance between tube plates as 12 ft 6 in. Within the boiler were thirty-six large superheater flue tubes and 283 smoke tubes, all welded directly into the tube plates following some expansion after insertion. This gave a total tube heating surface of 2,127 sq ft.

An external multi-valve poppet-type regulator valve was attached to a studded steel flange welded to the upper left-hand shoulder of the front ring.

Taken before the firebox assembly was completed, this view is looking rearwards from within the firebox to where the offset firehole opening was provided. At this stage the firebox casing had yet to be welded to the boiler. Had this already been done, the photograph would have been impossible due to the presence of the thermic syphons

J.G. Click/National Railway Museum

Two standard 6 in diameter Ross-pop safety valves were located on the top centre line at the rear end of the parallel centre ring. These were set to 280 psi.

It was with the rear section of the boiler that Bulleid departed from convention. He considered orthodox boiler stays a source of trouble and thus sought a cheaper method in both construction and maintenance. Accordingly, the customary water-jacketed firebox design was discarded and instead the top of the firebox was formed by an extension of the tapered barrel of the boiler in the shape of a slightly downward-sloping drum of segment section. The underside of this thus formed the firebox crown. This drum was butt-welded onto the rear ring as well as having a number of flexible rod stays. Conventional stays were provided between the top and bottom sections of the firebox top.

To restore some of the heating surface lost by this exercise, four Nicholson-type thermic syphons each equally spaced 1 ft 4 in apart were provided. In addition to yielding an additional 260 sq ft of heating surface they served to further anchor the firebox to the boiler. Each of the syphons drew water from just forward of the rear barrel ring, with a wash-out plug being directly on the elbow bend. Adjacent to the longest of the syphon necks was a downward pointing flange pipe to which was attached the manually operated blow-down valve associated with the TIA water treatment equipment. A total of thirty wash-out plugs were provided at strategic intervals on the firebox segment drum and front tube plate.

Firebox backhead showing its position relative to the bunker opening and firehole door. Notice the number of controls and gauges on the firebox crown is minimal. The four-spoked handwheels protruding from the floor are the water and steam controls for the injectors

J.G. Click/National Railway Museum

A rear view of the boiler and firebox assembly secured within the frames. Again the cross-bracing is obvious, which will later support the water and fuel bunkers

J.G. Click/National Railway Museum

To contain the fire was a fabricated single-sheet box welded directly to the boiler. Supported on a rectangular base frame of angled steel, the front and side sheets were straightforward flat plates suitably stiffened by a lattice of steel strips welded to the outer faces. The rear was more complicated and was fabricated of six triangular steel plates to produce an angled back. In the left-hand rear face was a steam-operated firehole door similar to that fitted to the Pacifics. Butterfly-type twin doors were provided and operated by a pedal on the fireman's cab floor. A manual back-up lever was also provided and attached to the doors themselves.

Welded to the interior of the firebox was a defined pattern of steel lugs intended to support the refractory firebrick lining. As originally designed the firebox had a generous grate area of 43 sq ft, the grate being of the rocking type and controlled by the fireman. The ashpan was also of steel sheet and of the double hopper type. Each hopper had two half-width 'flip-over' quadrant-shaped dump doors.

Air flow to the grate was via dampers of the same size at front and rear under the control of the fireman. The existence of dampers to both front and rear was necessary due to the original intention of not turning the engine between duties. The uncluttered midships location, not unlike the well-known articulated Garrett designs, allowed full advantage to be taken of the space available for the ashpan.

Provision was made for two boiler feed clacks, although in practice only one was used. This was mounted on the right-hand shoulder amidships of the front ring. A large eight-valve steam combine, with four wheel-operated and four lever-operated shut-off valves, was shoulder-mounted on the left-hand side at the front end of the tapered barrel portion.

Additionally, with the driver's controls segregated, the rear backhead was singularly devoid of fitments, the exception being a pair of water gauges which, when showing 1 in of water, equated to a 3 in covering of the firebox crown. Also within the fireman's compartment was the three-way TIA control and boiler pressure steam gauge.

The principal boiler-mounting cradle was a very substantial fabricated steel support, located immediately ahead of the firebox and straddling the syphon necks. Similar but smaller mountings were welded to the underside close to the front of the first ring. The underside of each of the support mountings was flat and each bore down onto special 'Mintex' insulating pads located on each side of the frame stretchers. These were clamped in place but also slid to cater for boiler expansion. The boiler centre line was 9 ft 4 in from rail level. To reduce heat loss, the boiler and firebox were lagged with a fibreglass material which was held in place with thin iron wire. Additionally, the firebox was first sheeted with an aluminium foil paper before being covered with the insulating material. On completion, but before being lagged, a hydraulic test to 350 psi was undertaken, followed by a 290 psi steam test.

Feedwater

TIA-treated water was used to feed the boiler with the chemical carried in a tank atop the main water tank. This chemical reservoir was also fitted with a warming pipe. The manually-operated blow-down equipment was intended to be activated by the fireman for half a minute every thirty miles, earlier experience with the Pacifics having found that an automatic blow-down valve was insufficient to expel the mud and sludge which collected in the lower parts of the boiler. A recorder fitted in the fireman's compartment registered each time the blow-down valve was activated.

Viewed from the underside of the main frames, the lower section of the boiler is visible which has been lagged. Notice also the TIA blow-down pipe. To the rear is the rocking grate

J.G. Click/National Railway Museum

The treated water was fed into the boiler by two Davies and Metcalfe No. 11 Monitor-type injectors. These were mounted beneath the well of the fireman's compartment. Water and steam handles then protruded through the floor into the central compartment. Provision for viewing the operation of the injectors was by holes cut into the floor while an electric light beneath the floor allowed for the same to seen during darkness.

Smokebox

Since the smokebox was concealed beneath the outer body casing it was designed to be solely functional. Fabricated from $\frac{1}{4}$ in plate with a thicker plate used for the floor, it traced an irregular octagonal pattern and was mated with the similar fitment on the front of the boiler barrel. At the top the smokebox was flat in section, upon which two vacuum reserve reservoirs were mounted.

To the front the smokebox was flat, to which the smokebox door was attached. This took the form of an oval with a flattened top, the shape being dictated by the design of the smokebox. Within the smokebox was mounted a Gresham & Craven single-cone vacuum ejector. The combined chimney and liner was of the convergent/divergent pattern and of large diameter to suit the design of the Bulleid modified Lemaitre

Boiler and smokebox assembly. The latter assumes its unusual shape at the front due to it being purely functional and having no aesthetic pretensions

J.G. Click/National Railway Museum

Smokebox and boiler assembly suitably lagged, with the front cab added

J.G. Click/National Railway Museum

Inside the smokebox, showing the multiple-jet blastpipe as well as the convoluted main steampipe leading to the cylinders. Atop the smokebox the available space has been utilized to mount the vacuum brake reservoir cylinders. Standing to the left is a plank of timber left by a fitter, which did not form part of the design!
J.G. Click/National Railway Museum

multiple-jet exhaust system. Top diameter of the chimney was 2 ft 5 in. When in position the chimney top was 12 ft 8 in from rail level. The body casing was attached to the chimney by an additional 1 in wide flange.

The superheater header was mounted in the rear upper portion of the smokebox and accommodated four vertical rows of nine double-run elements. An additional 454 sq ft of heating surface was provided.

The smokebox plates were covered with thick 'Magnesia' lagging blocks while, to help reduce heat radiation into the front driver's cab, an insulated 'firedoor' was attached to the smokebox door. The locking handles protruded through this insulating material.

Fuel bunker and water tank

The designed capacity of 4,000 gallons of water and 4 tons of coal were carried in an integral tank/bunker assembly welded directly onto the main frame structure. The water tank arrangements were divided into three principal components: a main tank augmented by a secondary slab tank on the right-hand side and also what came to be dubbed a 'mantle shelf' tank near the central firing compartment.

The main tank and coal bunker were centrally disposed and situated between the central fireman's cab and the driver's (No. 2 end) rear cab. In construction and layout the

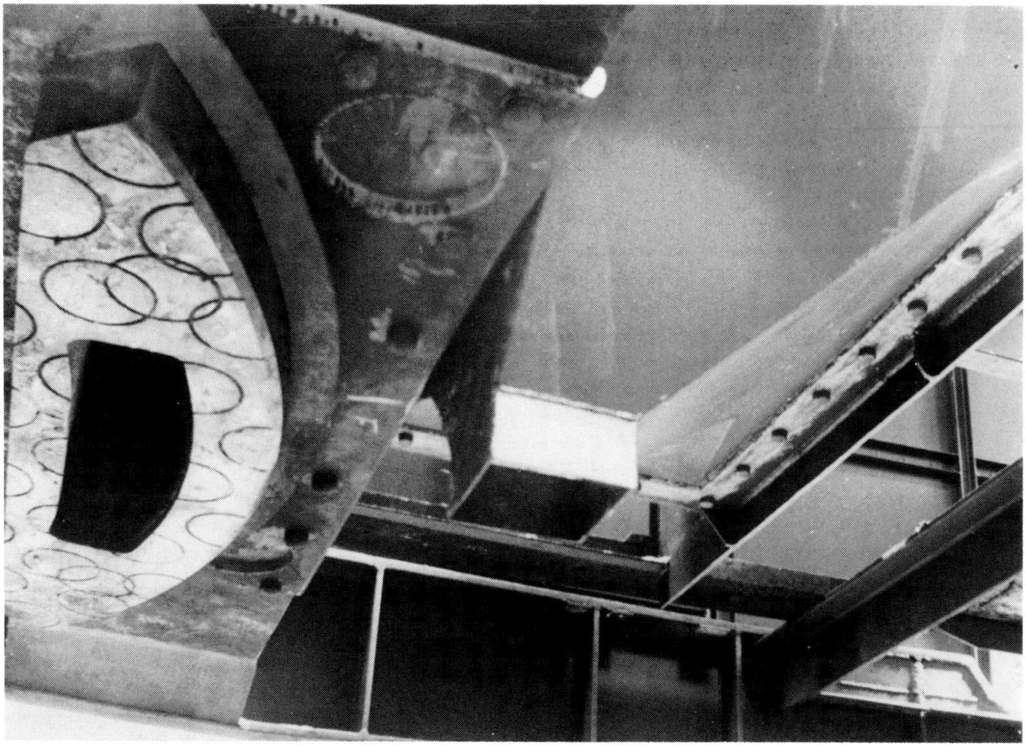

A rare view showing the bottom of the open duct for emptying the smokebox. To the left is the smokebox mounting pad

J.G. Click/National Railway Museum

With the main frame components in position, the bunker and water tanks are added. The position of the bunker is obvious, although not so apparent is the mantle shelf tank extending around the side of the firebox

J.G. Click/National Railway Museum

main tank and bunker was not unlike that of a conventional all-welded steel tender. The coal supply was in a bunker in the forward portion of the tank. This took the form of an asymmetrical hopper intended to self-trim the coal forward to the actual coal hole which, unlike normal practice, faced across the main structure. Ahead and immediately beneath this was the shovel plate.

Aft of the shovel plate the bunker panel extended to the full height of the casing profile and was fitted with a single door slightly over 3 ft 3 in × 1 ft 9 in, through which access could be gained to the coal bunker. Within the fireman's compartment was a water gauge.

Beneath the coal bunker the area was braced by a complex web of steel stretchers intended to act as baffles as well as absorb the loads created by water surge. An irregular-shaped sump plate was welded to the underside of the main water tank which combined a water feed well and strainer unit feeding the injector supply.

The integral slab side tank was located on the offside of the main water tank and was slightly higher than the level of the main frames. Nominally 1 ft 3 in wide it was curved to that of the outer casing. The mantle shelf tank, dubbed so because of its shape, height and location, was built integral with the offside slab tank and of the same height. It enveloped the lower half of the rear firebox panelling to curve forward along the nearside firebox frame. It carried precious little water but was intended to afford an additional heat barrier between the hot sides of the firebox and corridor and the fireman's compartment. Each tank was connected with the next. The handbrake was bolted to the front face of the main end tank panel.

A rare view of the opposite side of the engine, showing part of the slab water tank located vertically against the main frames. Notice also the smokebox door hinge just visible to the rear of the cab side sheets
J.G. Click/National Railway Museum

Reversing arrangement

The necessity to reverse both bogies simultaneously meant the reversing gear on 'Leader' was a complex affair.

Reversing was achieved by means of a steam cylinder rigidly attached to the main frames which then, by a series of gears, shafts, universal joints and splined shafts, transmitted the desired steam cut-off to each bogie.

This steam cylinder was of the standard steam and oil hydraulic locking arrangement supported beneath a fabricated carrier frame welded to the underside of the main frame belly on the left-hand side of the engine. From this a reduced diameter piston rod extension operated the cut-off indicators in both driving cabs.

All the working parts of the reversing arrangement were enclosed in individual oil baths and flood-lubricated. The weight shaft sector arms, gears and bearings shared an extension of the main transmission oil bath on the 'front' bogie but, due to the staggered chain drive arrangement, the 'rear' bogie components were housed in a separate enclosure. Small rectangular oil bath boxes were fitted around the inner bearings of the power bogie drive shafts. The lower half of the main reversing oil bath was readily removable for routine maintenance and included a bolted circular inspection cover.

Brakes – control system

The brake control system together with the actual brake rigging was possibly the most sophisticated ever fitted to a steam locomotive. It consisted of an automatic vacuum brake system incorporating a new patented automatic ejector control. In place of the roar of a conventional ejector used to create and maintain vacuum, 'Leader' was fitted with high and low pressure reservoirs and an automatic ejector system. When a drain was made on the low pressure 21 in reservoirs these were automatically replenished from the two high pressure 25 in reservoirs located atop the smokebox. This continued until both had reached the same level at which point the system would automatically charge in a series of small bursts, shutting itself off automatically when 25 in had been restored.

In practice the control system was both reliable and effective. Hence, when standing at the platform, the familiar roar from the continuous operation of the small ejector was replaced by intermittent short bursts from the single-core ejector – a new sound and totally unique to 'Leader'. Allied to this the fully compensated clasp brakes on each of the twelve wheels gave the driver confidence in control and braking power.

Casing

The main frame structure supported a full-length sheet steel casing which enveloped the whole of the 'top works'. In plan it traced the same profile as that of the main frame structure and was not dissimilar to that of the Bulleid coach design. It was attached by two methods, either welding or bolts, dependent upon anticipated service requirements.

For descriptive purposes the casing was subdivided into three parts, a centre parallel section through which the cross-section profile remained constant, and two tapered (in

Steam/hydraulic reversing cylinders which, through a system of rods and gears, imparted the same steam admission and exhaust movement to the sleeve valves of each power bogie. The ashpan discharge was via the hopper doors which alleviated the need for tiresome manual cleaning

J.G. Click/National Railway Museum

Seen in position the reversing gear is associated with its necessary linkage. Modellers should note the reversing gear was needed on one side of the locomotive only

J.G. Click/National Railway Museum

plan) end sections. In these the profile radii remained constant but the overall width reduced from 9 ft to 8 ft at the extremities. Modellers should note that the casing sides are not flat but describe a 50 ft inward-curving radius.

The front portion provided the enclosure for the larger of the two driving cabs, bow-fronted and with three flat facets, each furnished with a brass-framed window. Only the centre window could be opened although all three windows shared a common rain gutter strip across the top.

Access to the cab was via a 1 ft 10 in opening on either side, each with a roller wheel-type sliding door which followed the same profile as the casing end. There were no windows in the doors, but above each door was another rain gutter strip.

Ventilation could be controlled by a 2 ft wide, fore and aft, sliding roof panel which gave a maximum opening of 2 ft 3 in.

Within the cab was a wooden floor and a maximum cab height of 6 ft 6 in at the engine centre line. This decreased towards the sides, as seen in the photographs. From the cab front (No. 1 end) to the smokebox door the distance was 8 ft 9 in, which allowed adequate room for opening the smokebox door.

The problem of ash disposal from the smokebox was considered at an early stage in the design, it being recognized that a more efficient method than existing manual means was desirable.

In the wake of the trial with No. 1896 it was first suggested that an ash duct of similar design should be provided on 'Leader'. However, the space required for such a chute was needed for the steam turbine-driven oil pumps and the eventual ducted route was suspect due to its shallow angle of descent allied to bogie movement.

As fitted the chute was of straightforward fabrication, bolted to the underside of the smokebox base to discharge the ash between the oil baths through a 6 in square exit. It was under external mechanical control. The chute was later sealed and recourse made to manual smokebox cleaning.

The central fireman's compartment, seen here with the framework added for the outer casing. The larger opening to the right is for the door
J.G. Click/National Railway Museum

A rare view, looking along the corridor within the engine from No. 1 end to the fireman's compartment and beyond to No. 2 end. At the time the photograph was taken the corridor was obstructed by various tools and equipment although it was intended to be relatively free. In service further obstruction would be caused by the necessary addition of weights to assist in the evening out of the weight distribution
J.G. Click/National Railway Museum

The exterior casing was of thin steel sheet stiffened where necessary and supported in cross-section by formers. This was then welded to the main frame structure. At the rear the roof section was cut away to suit the profile of the coal bunker as well as the water tank filler and TIA container. The rear cab assembly was necessarily shortened to just 4 ft due to the intrusion of the water tank and bunker assembly.

Access to the bunker and top plate for water filling and TIA inspection was via the cab roof ventilation aperture at No. 2 end and accordingly three 15 in wide steel rungs were welded to the tank end plate. Hand-holds were also provided at the tank end.

A number of bolted panels were provided in the casing where this covered the smokebox, boiler, fireman's cab and water and bunker assemblies. These were to enable service access to various components.

Apart from the chimney opening within the casing, further openings were provided for the safety valves, a single exposed whistle and thirteen washout plugs. All of these were on the boiler centre line which was necessarily offset 6 in from the engine centre line.

In the casing portion covering the firebox, two lines of $6\frac{1}{2}$ in × $6\frac{1}{2}$ in vents were cut along the 'flattened' shoulder portion on both sides. These had individual sliding shutters and were above the corridor space formed by the offset boiler and bunker. Within the fireman's cab and on the engine centre line was a rectangular sliding ventilator similar to those fitted to the driving cabs.

Entry to the fireman's cab was by a single sliding door, similar to the driver's door but having a glass window. Alongside this was a triple sliding window not dissimilar to those fitted to the Pacifics in later years. Both the door and windows were protected by rain strips. Due to loading gauge restrictions it was not possible to fit a normal handrail and instead a vertical gulley was formed in the casing and fitted with a sunken handrail.

Within the central fireman's compartment the floor level was lowered to form a well which created more room within the compartment. When entering from the outside the fireman stepped down into his cab which was provided with a wooden floor having cross-planks in similar fashion to the driving cabs.

Taken from inside the smokebox: the smokebox door can be seen swung open to the right. This is a view of the cab at No. 1 end prior to final fitting out

J.G. Click/National Railway Museum

With the interior components in position, the supports for the exterior casing are added. The 'mantle shelf' water tank also shows up well in this view

J.G. Click/National Railway Museum

Electrics

Instrumentation lamps, inspection lamps, cab and other illumination, together with route indicator lamps, were all electrically lit. The 24 V supply was provided by a single Stones-type TG1 steam turbine generator of 1 kW maximum output. This was mounted in the corridor of the body structure alongside the boiler and beneath the regulator valve. A steam supply was obtained from the boiler manifold via a governor unit while the exhaust was taken directly into the smokebox.

Six electric lamps were provided for headcode illumination at each end of the locomotive. Traditional steel brackets to support the more familiar headcode discs – or reversion to oil lamps in case of emergency – were also provided. The lamps were operated from banks of toggle switches in the driving compartments.

The turbine generator also provided power for an electrically-driven windscreen wiper, clearing the driver's window only at each end cab.

Controls and instrumentation

The arrangement of controls and instrumentation was similar in both driving cabs. The exception to this was that the actual driving position was 'in line' with the corridor. Accordingly, when running with No. 1 end leading the driver was on the left-hand side and with No. 2 end leading he was seated at the right. In the latter case signal sighting was unaffected due to the uninterrupted forward vision.

The controls in each cab were carefully laid out and could be reached by the driver from a single padded and swivelling seat.

Power bogies – pivots

One of the most interesting and unique features was the design of the two power bogies. Spaced at 34 ft centres, they had no physical centre pivots, but relied on four very substantial segment-shaped bearing pads riveted to the top surfaces of the bogie assembly and located on the longitudinal and transverse centre lines of the bogie. These fabricated steel pads were lined with gunmetal bearing faces, machined with a matrix of oil grooves.

A heavily reinforced outer 'fence' was welded to each of the segments to provide both radial pivot location and a means of power transference. It should be noted that the drawgear was attached to the power bogie buffer beams and not the main frames. Accordingly, power from the leading bogie had to pass through both front and rear pivots while each of these items had to be capable of withstanding either power or braking loads from both ends.

Similar, but unfenced, pads were attached to the underside of the main frame structure. One of the advantages of the pivotless bogie was that it allowed the main steam pipe to pass through each bogie adjacent to the vertical centre axis – the point of least movement – while sufficient flexibility in the design allowed the locomotive to negotiate curves down to a minimum radius of $5\frac{1}{2}$ chains (121 yd).

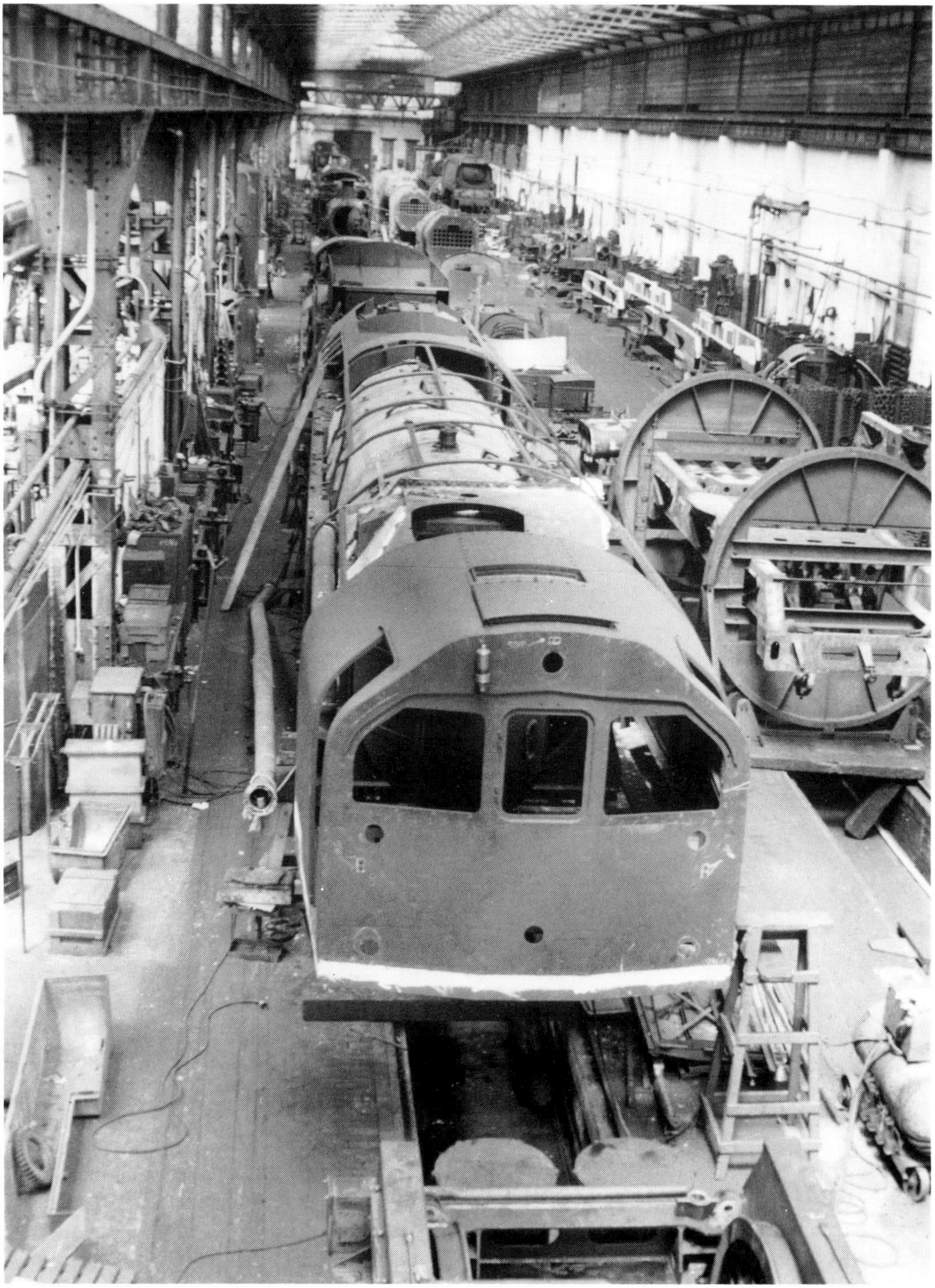

Seen from above, the exterior casing is being added. To the right is the circular welding frame used in the construction of the power bogies

J.G. Click/National Railway Museum

The casing complete, with the added bonus of a brief glimpse inside the cab at No. 2 end. The steps allowing access to the roof are also just visible within the cab
J.G. Click/National Railway Museum

A power bogie seen from above, with the temporary addition of an external steam supply. Notice the body-mounting rubbing plates and the position of the main steampipe
J.G. Click/National Railway Museum

Main steampipe on the power bogie. This was later lagged to reduce heat loss. The leaf spring visible afforded damping for one side of one axle and a cover was later provided so that the whole was working within an oil-tight environment

J.G. Click/National Railway Museum

Bogie frame assembly

The bogie frame assemblies, like that of the main frame, were of welded steel fabrication. Both front and rear units were identical and each consisted of two box-section side frames braced by a complex of stretchers. These included the leading and trailing end beams, front and rear slide bar supports and inner and outer support stretchers. The last two named also supported the valve gear, motion and brake parts. Into the bogies were welded the cylinder fabrications, which formed the major structural component part. Other items such as oil baths were also added by weld as construction proceeded.

Within the bogie side frames, which were hollow box-sections, an elongated triangular access hole was provided at each of the six spring 'stations'. These were necessarily stiffened and lipped, to which complementary-shaped steel cover plates were bolted.

At the leading end the frames increased in depth on the underside to form a large area to which the cylinders were welded.

The buffer beams were 7 ft wide and of steel plate. Two additional pairs of 1 in thick steel gussets were welded to the top plate extremities and were drilled with 2 in diameter holes which acted as lifting lugs.

Bogie side frame assembly, with the horn guide pedestals visible. Notice part of the movement of the reversing gear, while the leaf springs have yet to be added
J.G. Click/National Railway Museum

The rear beam was of similar construction and in addition fronted three rear-facing triangular-shaped brackets to support the large brake cylinders.

Steam and exhaust pipes on the power bogies

To absorb bogie movement the steampipes were of convoluted steel, so giving an amount of movement without the fear of rupture. Both pipes passed down through the bogie in a 'swan-neck' turn, close to the hypothetical pivot point. They then plunged down through the oil bath to face the cylinders via an elbow turn. To reduce heat loss, the entire main steampipe run, with the exception of flange joints fitted where necessary, was lagged in metallic asbestos twine.

The layout of the exhaust initially formed an integral part of the assembly since it was welded into the structure. A 7 in internal diameter fabricated steel tube carried the exhaust from the cylinders until it was 'teed' into a short stub tube. The exhaust emerged from the bogies via a rectangular duct bolted to the top of the stretcher plate ahead of the front bogie bearing pad.

The obvious difficulty of locating and maintaining the precise siting of the various sub-assemblies during welding was overcome with the use of a simple rotary welding cradle to which the frames were attached and then turned to the most convenient position ready for the next item to be added.

Horn guide pedestals

A pair of hollow flange-mounted cylindrical steel pedestal guides of 5½ in diameter were attached to the underside of each bogie frame.

Axleboxes

All six axles were carried on Timken double-bow taper roller bearings. The utilization of power transmission chains to connect the coupled wheels eliminated the need to maintain precise axle centres as would be the case with a conventional chassis fitted with coupling rods. Bulleid used this to advantage to 'resilient mount' the axle assemblies.

Wheels and axles

The six driving and coupled wheels of each power unit were of 5 ft 1 in diameter and the same size as on the Q1 class. They bore the familiar Bulleid hallmark of BFB wheels which gave a more continuous support to the steel tyres compared with a spoke arrangement. Tyres were coned at a 1 in 20 inclination.

By substituting chains for coupling rods the need for crankpins was dispensed with. Similarly, since the three-throw forged steel crankshaft of each unit was phased with 120° crank settings, no balance weights were required.

The three-throw driving axle referred to was of hollow construction. The overall length was no less than 8 ft 2⅝ in which was necessary to accommodate the final drive sprockets. These were pressed on and secured with threaded flange caps screwed into the axle ends. Anti-rotation was afforded by a special hexagon/pentagon design, the brainchild of Reg Curl, at the time Chief Draughtsman at Eastleigh.

Preparation of one of the final drive sprockets within Brighton Works
J.G. Click/National Railway Museum

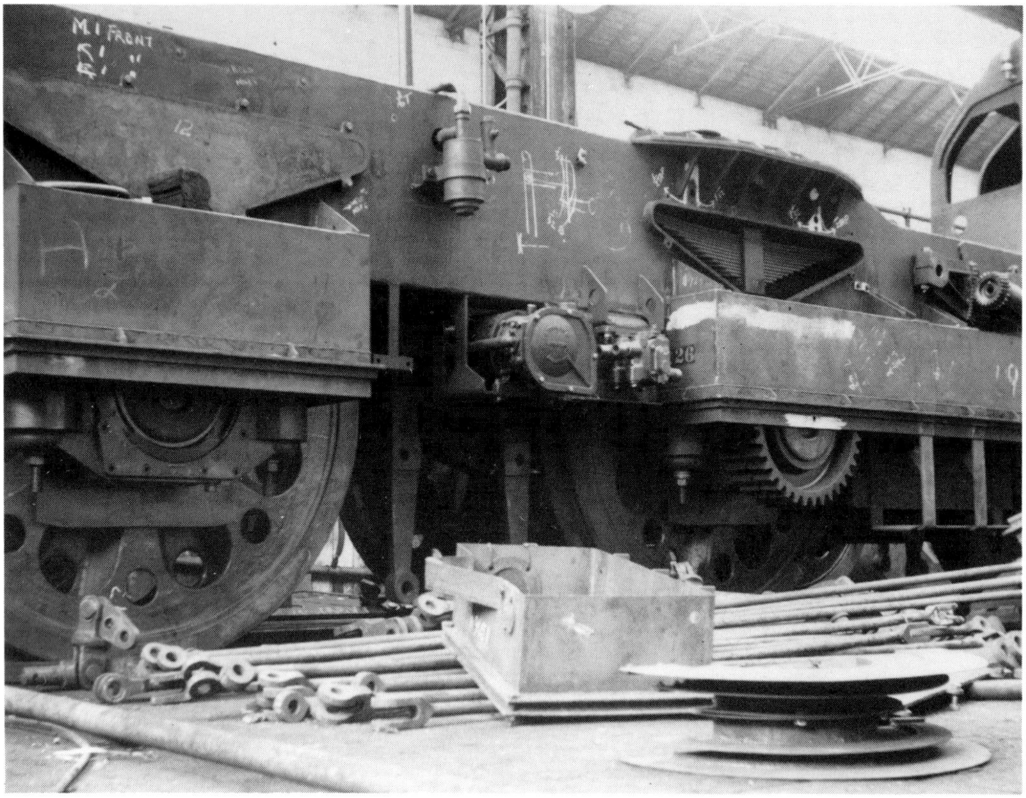

Wheels and axles in position and also the top covers of the final drive axle baths
J.G. Click/National Railway Museum

The driving wheel centres were pressed and keyed using a pressure of 120 tons. Leading and trailing axle arrangements were similar except the axles were plain, although again hollow.

It may be of interest to record that the cast wheel centres were pressed onto the axle ends without the tyres being added, and, although the axles were asymmetrical, by reversal they could be used for either leading or trailing application on each bogie.

Chain transmission drive

A major deviation from normal locomotive practice was to couple the axles using chains and sprockets. This was an attempt to remove the inherent disadvantage of conventional cranks and coupling rods; namely, their inability to transmit constant torque throughout a revolution. Instead, 'Morse' multi-link inverted tooth transmission chains were used.

However, because the chassis layout dictated that the sprockets should be on the outer extremities of the driving axles, the confines of the loading gauge would not permit sufficient space to drive both forwards and backwards on each side. The only solution, therefore, was to employ a staggered arrangement by driving forward to the leading axle on the right-hand side and rearwards to the trailing axle on the left-hand side.

The rear of a power bogie, at the time still with a number of components to be fitted. Notice the axle-driven mechanical lubricator

J.G. Click/National Railway Museum

Bogie spring rigging

For the spring rigging, laminated springs were chosen as being a particularly attractive application. They had the advantage of being both simply and neatly housed in the box section of the bogie frames. Here they performed under more or less ideal conditions, away from the enemies of grit, ash and dust and with the added bonus of being flood-lubricated.

Cylinders

The three cylinders in each of the two power bogies were each of 12½ in bore and 15 in stroke. They were also unique for modern-day steam traction in that the steam distribution was controlled by sleeve valves within the cylinder bores.

Each three-cylinder assembly was in a steel fabricated structure welded directly into the bogie frame, thus eliminating the usual array of fitting bolts. The assembly consisted of three steel tubes welded between two substantial end plates. They had an overall length of 4 ft 2 in, a considerable distance when compared with the 15 in stroke.

To produce a central admission annulus and independent exhaust steam annuli at both ends of the cylinders, the three assemblies were rolled and welded from ½ in steel plate in the form of open triple-bolted sections.

Between each of the three annulus assemblies were welded separating plates and, as with No. 2039, the cylinders were enveloped in a full-length steam jacket. Prior to

A power bogie nearing completion. Several gangs of men were involved in the construction of the engine, with one concentrating on the bogies while others worked on the main superstructure assembly
J.G. Click/National Railway Museum

Cylinder block prior to the fitting of the Mechanite liners
J.G. Click/National Railway Museum

Machining a sleeve valve for 'Leader'. The various port openings were first drilled before opening out to the required size
J.G. Click/National Railway Museum

welding thirteen admission and thirteen exhaust ports were cut into the inside edge of each separating plate.

The cylinder assembly was inclined downwards from the front towards the crank axle at an angle of 1 in 8. Cast-iron liners were pressed into each cylinder, with holes provided to correspond to the admission and exhaust ports.

The sleeve valves were merely tubes of cast Mechanite, a fine grain cast iron, machined to a sliding fit within the liners. They were then bored to house the pistons, with ports cut circumferentially around each end of the sleeve. The innermost rows were for steam admission and the outer ports for exhaust. Rings were provided at intervals between the sleeve valve and cylinder liner.

Cast-iron piston heads were used, each having four sealing rings. Fabricated covers were provided at both ends, although these differed considerably in design.

Motion

The piston rods and crossheads were machined from a one-piece forging. Each rod was a nominal $2\frac{3}{4}$ in diameter and secured to the piston head by a flange nut fitted with a split taper pin for final security.

Coupling rods were of 'I' section and 5 ft 9 in long. These were steel forgings of the simple strap type.

Sleeve valve motion

The sleeve valve motion was designed to give a variable figure-of-eight mode of operation. This was derived from two sources: a variable reciprocating motion controlled by an adaptation of Bulleid's patented valve gear, and a constant part-rotary or oscillating motion. This latter effect was imparted to the drive using the 'described use of a lever' principle and was intended to distribute the lubrication and reduce wear. The combination of these two modes thus produced the required movement.

The Bulleid gear itself derived its motion from an independent three-throw crankshaft, chain-driven from the main crank axle. Since the main crank axle was a one-piece forging, the driven sprocket was a two-piece split gear secured by bolts. This gear was clamped between the centre and right-hand crank.

An idler gear was provided which was supported by a bracket attached to the main bogie stretcher. The valve gear crankshaft was machined from a one-piece Mechanite casting and consisted of three unbalanced cranks again set at 120°. The shaft was carried on split bearings which were attached to fabricated steel supports extending rearwards from the main stretcher.

The eccentric gear was a Bulleid speciality and he was able to reduce the frictional losses of conventional large eccentrics and sheaves, which he referred to as 'band-brakes'. Accordingly, a vertical drive was used to oscillate the expansion link, so

Power bogie front end, with part of the sleeve valve reciprocating mechanism visible as well as the projecting lugs from the three sleeve valves. Notice also the bogie lifting points
J.G. Click/National Railway Museum

Seen from the front end the reciprocating mechanism has been added to two of the sleeve valves. A recently found film of a bogie steam test on 'Leader' affords a glimpse of this reciprocating mechanism at work and is a fascinating insight into the engineering of the machine
J.G. Click/National Railway Museum

enabling the cut-off to be varied. The eccentrics used were designed on the radial engine connecting rod principle, using one master rod. The expansion links were similarly miniaturized.

Each sleeve was driven by an arm rigidly attached to the outer radius of the upper sleeve.

Oscillating gear

The initial drive for this was taken from the centre crosshead, not unlike the lap/lead arrangement of Walschaerts valve gear.

A drop arm was attached to the right-hand side of the crosshead and used to drive a pendulum lever via a short link and so remove the angularity of the lever, each of the three sleeves being fitted with a driving beam.

In operation the vertical movement described by the oscillating arm and derived from the pendulum lever, lifted two die-blocks. This raised the right-hand jaw beam assembly together with the right-hand side of the centre jaw beam assembly and caused the right-hand sleeve to partially rotate in an anti-clockwise direction, seen from the front. The centre sleeve adopted a clockwise rotation.

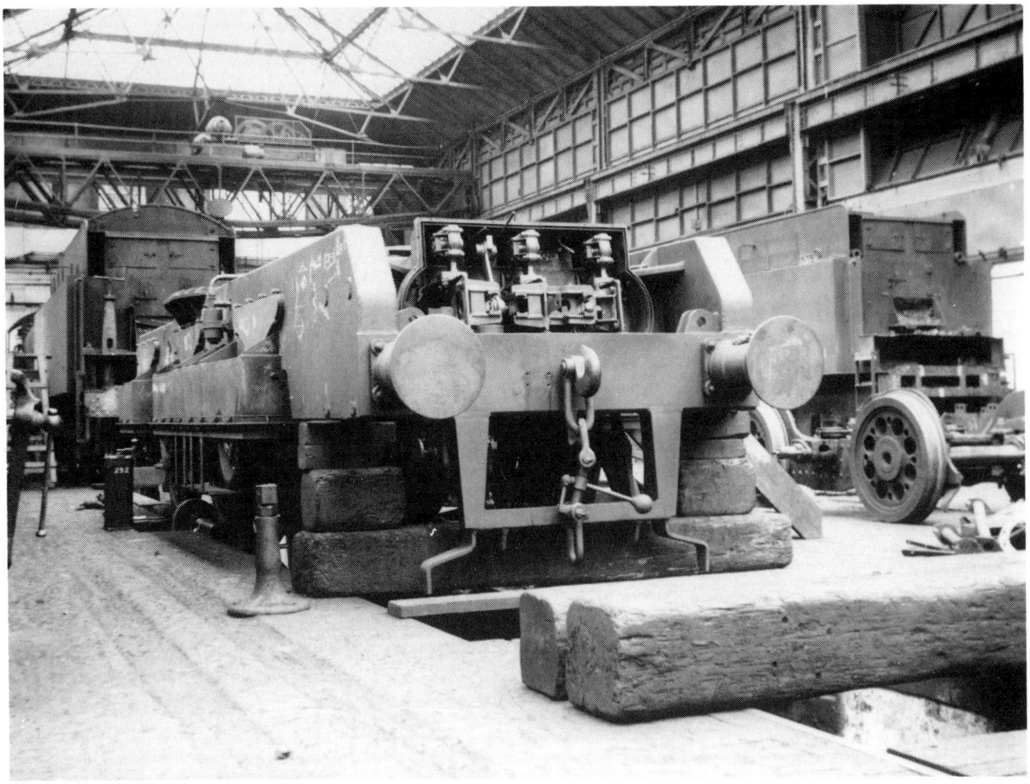

A power bogie almost completed and with the rear casing added
J.G. Click/National Railway Museum

Being diametrically opposite, the left-hand jaw beam assembly was thus moved downwards and took with it the die-block fitted to the trunnion of the left-hand jaw beam assembly. This caused the left-hand sleeve to rotate anti-clockwise. When 'Leader' first ran a cover was provided to the sleeve valve oscillating gear.

Cylinder cocks

The emission of exhaust steam condensate from the chimney together with condensate in the cylinders is both undesirable and hazardous. In the 'Leader' design the problem was even more critical due to the long pipe runs involved in getting the live steam to, and the exhaust steam from, No. 2 bogie. Bulleid took steps to both prevent and reduce the problem.

Prevention was by ensuring the fixed steam and exhaust pipes were lagged, while the design of the cylinders allowed for a steam flow around the admission and exhaust annuli. Two cylinder drain cocks were provided at the front and rear of each cylinder assembly. In addition, a third drain cock was attached to the main steam pipe elbows prior to entering the cylinders. Thus, by opening the cocks and cracking the regulator, steam could flow through the pipes, warming these and the cylinders and raising them to working temperature before being thrown out of the drain cocks.

Control of the drain cocks was via a linkage controlled by a quadrant-mounted hand

The incomplete No. 36003 being towed into Brighton Works for cutting up on 23 May 1951. In its embryo form the slab side tank shows up clearly in the photograph

Don Broughton Collection

Seen from the rear, the bogie vacuum cylinders have been added. Notice the access to the oil bath via the rectangular opening. In the background is 'West Country' Pacific No. 34017 *Ilfracombe*. Although none of the 'Leader' class ever carried the names intended for them, recent research has uncovered a drawing of a works plate for the class. This was to have been 8 in long and, as well as the date and location of building, would have also carried the names of Bulleid, Granshaw and Cocks, the patent numbers for the boiler and for the valve gear. It is believed this item was never cast

J.G. Click/National Railway Museum

lever in each cab. As an additional safeguard, large blow-off valves were fitted to the front and rear covers of each cylinder. Under test at Brighton the crew maintained that the exhaust upon starting was more free of exhaust 'rain' than with a conventional steam locomotive.

Lubrication

Two independent lubrication systems were used on each bogie unit: a high pressure system for the cylinders, and a continuous-flow system for the remaining working components.

Included in the high pressure system were the sleeve valves, cylinder liners and pistons, with the oil being delivered by three Wakefield No. 7 lubricators mounted on a welded carrier frame mounted on the right-hand side of each bogie. These were in turn driven by a link extending down from the sleeve valve oscillating gear. A series of copper pipes, valves and connectors then distributed the lubricant.

The flow system was of the Bulleid oil bath type which fed the entire engine unit of each bogie. The oil supply for this was obtained from a sump and then delivered under pressure by oil pumps driven by a steam turbine, again mounted externally on each bogie. Photographs reveal the location of these exterior components, with the steam turbine easily identified by the tell-tale emission of steam.

As well as lubricating the inside motion, separate oil baths were provided on the

Bogie vacuum cylinders from underneath together with their associated operating mechanism
J.G. Click/National Railway Museum

exterior of each bogie comprising two single and two double units. These enclosed the axleboxes, pedestal guides and roller bearings and, in the case of the double units, the final drive chain connecting the axles. The staggered arrangement of the chain drive, the reasons for which have been described earlier, accounted for the asymmetrical layout of the outside oil baths which are such a prominent feature of the 'Leader' design.

Brake rigging

Mounted on the rear of each bogie were two 24 in vacuum cylinders. These were connected via a 5 in shaft to the brake operating levers, pull rods and compensating beams which formed an identical arrangement on each bogie. Power braking was afforded to all wheels.

Sundries and draw gear

With all six wheels available for adhesion and also driven, the risk of slipping was negligible. Hence, sanding gear was not provided and, indeed, never found necessary.

The draw hook and coupling fitted to the two power bogies was of standard SR type cushioned by Spencer Moulton pads compressed at the rear of each beam by the securing nut.

Electric lamps fitted to the underside of the front and rear edges of the body structure provided illumination when coupling at night.

A pair of brass whistles was mounted one at each end of the locomotive adjacent to the topmost headcode indicator. These were independently operated from either end.

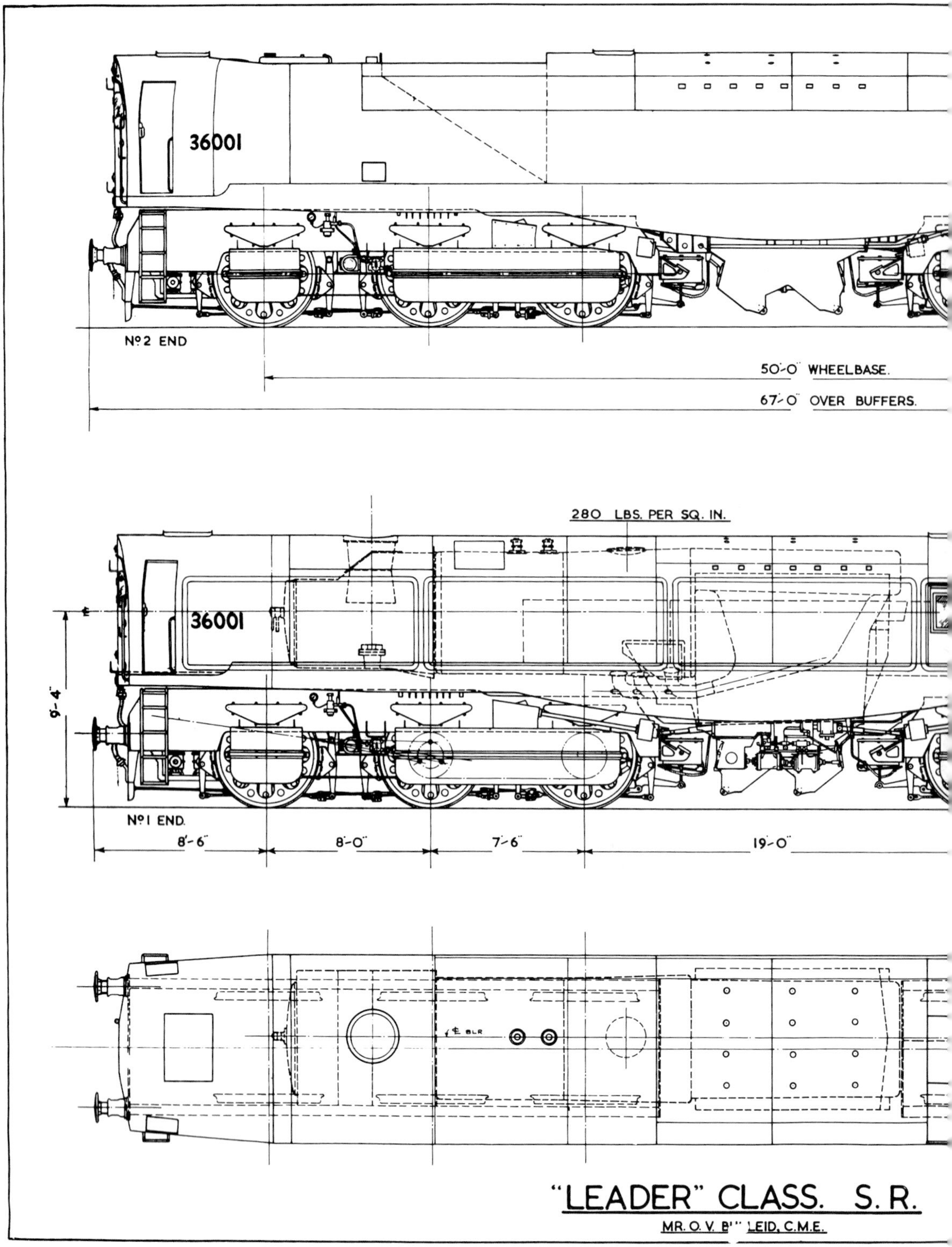
36001
Nº2 END
50'-0" WHEELBASE.
67'-0" OVER BUFFERS.
280 LBS. PER SQ. IN.
36001
9'-4"
Nº1 END
8'-6"
8'-0"
7'-6"
19'-0"
"LEADER" CLASS. S. R.

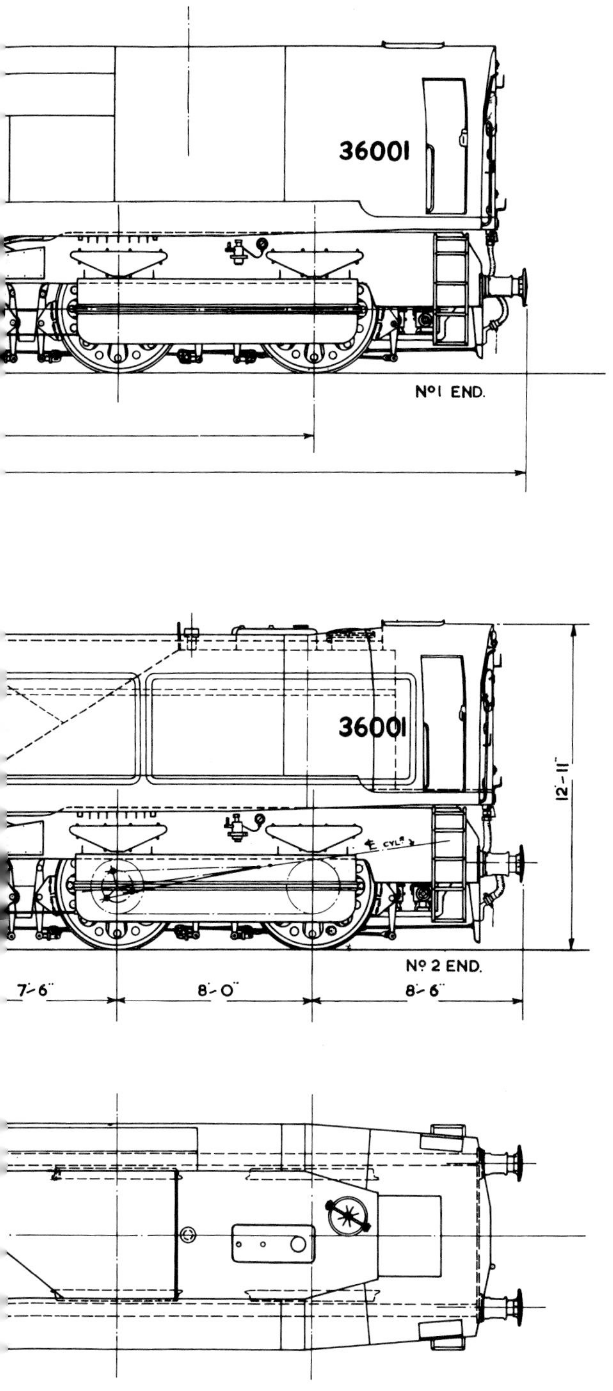

LEADING DIMENSIONS.

CYLINDERS: 3 PER BOGIE. 12¼" X 15".
MOTION: BULLEID. SLEEVE VALVES.
DIA. OF DRIVING WHEELS. 5'-1".
GRATE AREA. 43 SQ. FT.
4 NICHOLSON THERMIC SYPHONS.
TUBES: LARGE. 36 — 5¼" X 5/32".
SMALL. 283 — 1⅝" X 12 S.W.G.

HEATING SURFACE:	SMALL TUBES.	1508 SQ. FT.
	LARGE TUBES.	619 .. ..
	FIREBOX.	260 .. ..
TOTAL EVAPORATIVE.		2387 .. ..
SUPERHEATER.		454 .. ..
TOTAL HEATING SURFACE.		2841 .. ..

TRACTIVE EFFORT AT 85% B.P. 26300 LBS.
DESIGNED WEIGHT IN WORKING ORDER. 120 TONS.
WATER CAPACITY. 4000 GALLONS.
COAL CAPACITY. 4 TONS.

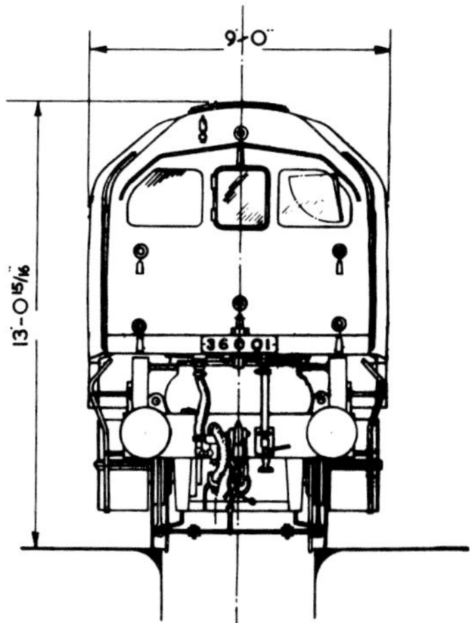

Nº1 END. L.H. DRIVE.
(Nº2 END. R.H. DRIVE.)

BIBLIOGRAPHY

Books

Bradley, D.L., *Locomotives of the LSWR and SR* (8 vols.), RCTS.
Holcroft, H., *Locomotive Adventure* (2 vols.), Ian Allan.
Robertson, K., *The Great Western Railway Gas Turbines: A Myth Exposed*, Alan Sutton Publishing, Gloucester, 1989.
Robertson, K., *Leader: Steam's Last Chance*, Alan Sutton Publishing, Gloucester, 1988.
Townroe, S.C., *Arthurs, Nelsons and Schools at Work*, Ian Allan, 1983.

Periodicals

The Journal of the Stephenson Locomotive Society
Proceedings of the Institution of Locomotive Engineers
Proceedings of the Institution of Mechanical Engineers
Railway Gazette
Railway Observer
Southern Railway Magazine

INDEX